W9-AHN-594

CALVIN AND HOBBES
SUNDAY PAGES 1985-1995

An Exhibition Catalogue by

BILL WATTERSON

Andrews McMeel Publishing

Kansas City

In cooperation with
The Ohio State University
Cartoon Research Library

 For information, write Andrews McMeel Publishing, LLC, an Andrews McMeel Universal company, 1130 Walnut Street, Kansas City, Missouri 64106.

ISBN-13: 978-0-7407-7793-6
ISBN-10: 0-7407-7793-9

Design: Frank Pauer

This catalogue accompanies the exhibition *Calvin and Hobbes: Sunday Pages 1985-1995* at The Ohio State University Cartoon Research Library from September 10, 2001, to January 15, 2002.

The exhibition was mounted with the support of The Ohio State University Libraries. All works in the exhibition are from the personal collection of the cartoonist, and we are grateful to him for lending them for this purpose. We also appreciate the contributions of Frank Pauer, Marilyn Scott, Erin Shipley, Dennis Toth, Rick VanBrimmer, and Richard Samuel West to the exhibit and this publication. Special thanks to Andrews McMeel Publishing for producing and distributing this book.

Cover: [unpublished watercolor of Calvin and Hobbes] Private collection. Watercolor on paper. 12 x 12.4 cm.

PREFACE

Everyone misses *Calvin and Hobbes*.

It reinvented the newspaper comic strip at a time when many had all but buried the funnies as a vehicle for fresh, creative work. Then Bill Watterson came along and reminded a new generation of what older readers and comic strip afficionados knew: A well-written and beautifully drawn strip is an intricate, powerful form of communication. And with *Calvin and Hobbes*, we had fun—just like readers of *Krazy Kat* and *Pogo* did. Opening the newspaper each day was an adventure. The heights of Watterson's creative imagination took us places we had never been. We miss that.

This book is published in conjunction with the first exhibition of original *Calvin and Hobbes* Sunday pages at The Ohio State University Cartoon Research Library. Although the work was created for reproduction, not for gallery display, it is a pleasure to see the cartoonist's carefully placed lines and exquisite brush strokes. In an attempt to share this experience with those who are unable to visit the exhibition, all of the original Sunday pages displayed are reproduced in color in this book so that every detail, such as sketch lines, corrections, and registration marks, are visible. On the opposite page the same comic strip is printed in full color. Because Watterson was unusually intentional and creative in his use of color, this juxtaposition provides *Calvin and Hobbes* readers the opportunity to consider the impact of color on its narrative and content.

When I first contacted Bill Watterson about the possibility of exhibiting his original work, I used the term "retrospective." He replied that we might be able to do an exhibit, but that calling it a retrospective made him uncomfortable since it has been only a few years since he stopped drawing the comic strip. He felt that a longer time was needed to put *Calvin and Hobbes* in the historical perspective implied by that term. Nonetheless, this show is a "look back" at the comic strip as we revisit favorites that we remember. *Calvin and Hobbes: Sunday Pages 1985-1995* is particularly interesting because each work that is included was selected by Bill Watterson. His comments about the thirty-six Sunday pages he chose are part of this volume. In addition, he reflects on *Calvin and Hobbes* from the perspective of six years, and his essay provides insights into his life as a syndicated cartoonist.

Reprint books of *Calvin and Hobbes* are nice to have, but the opportunity to see the original work and read Bill Watterson's thoughts about it is a privilege. He generously shared not only the art, but also his time and his thoughts. When I first reviewed the works included in the exhibit, I knew that everyone who visited it would begin with laughter and end with tears.

On behalf of all who enjoyed *Calvin and Hobbes*, thank you, Bill Watterson.

Lucy Shelton Caswell
Professor and Curator
The Ohio State University Cartoon Research Library
June 2001

CALVIN AND HOBBES SUNDAY PAGES 1985-1995

It's been five years since the end of *Calvin and Hobbes*, the longest time I can remember in which I haven't drawn cartoons. *Calvin and Hobbes* was a wonderful experience, but it was an all-consuming career. When I quit the strip, I put my cartoons in boxes, and jumped into other interests. I haven't really considered the strip since, so at the invitation to do this show, I thought it might be time to look back at some of my work.

My first reaction in going through my old cartoons was some amazement at the size and weight of the pile. For most successful comic strips, ten years is just a drop in the bucket, but even that amount of time yields a huge amount of material. It's no wonder that decade seems like a blur.

Going through my old strips is sort of like looking at old photographs of myself: they're personal and familiar, yet somewhat bizarre at the same time. There are cartoons I've drawn that are the equivalent of pictures of my younger self wearing yellow pants: I know I'm responsible for that, but what on earth was I thinking? As my tastes have changed, and as I've learned more, I imagine that I would do many strips quite differently today. Not better necessarily, but certainly differently. I was twenty-eight when *Calvin and Hobbes* was first published, and, of course, I would make other choices now at age forty-three.

It's also sort of strange to see a record of my own learning curve. Pick up a given strip, and I see how I struggled with various writing and drawing problems, or how I finally surmounted one. I remember sometimes feeling that the strip was better written than I could actually write, and better drawn than I could actually draw. I learned a great deal over the years by trying to push the strip beyond my own abilities, and I'm very proud that *Calvin and Hobbes* explored and developed all the way to the end. By the final years, I see naturalness or a sense of inevitability to the drawing and writing that is very satisfying. I'm more appreciative of this kind of grace since returning to the awkward stages of new learning curves.

Of course, I'd also say the times have caught up with some of my strips. It's frankly a little discouraging to see how ordinary some of them look now. When *Calvin and Hobbes* first appeared, it was somewhat surprising to treat reality as subjective, and to draw a strip with multiple viewpoints, juxtaposing Calvin's vision with what others saw. I did this simply as a way to put the reader in Calvin's head and to reveal his imaginative personality. Now these juxtapositions are a visual game for many comic strips, and after all these years, I suspect readers know where this sort of joke is headed as soon as they see it. The novelty cannot be recaptured.

Novelty, however, is probably overrated anyway. The *Calvin and Hobbes* strips that hold up best, to my eye anyway, are the ones where the characters seem big, vivid, and full of life, and where the strip's world seems genuine and inviting. Punchlines come and go, but something in the friendship between Calvin and Hobbes seems to hold a small piece of truth. Expressing something real and honest is, for me, the joy and the importance of cartooning.

The Sunday strips were usually the cartoons I had the most fun with, and for this show I've chosen a few Sunday strips from each year that I think show off the strip's strengths.

I have fond memories of reading the Sunday comics when I was a kid. As far as I was concerned, the Sunday comics were the whole reason for newspapers to exist. On weekdays, I read only the strips I liked; but on Sundays, I read them all, and often several times. The Sunday comics were always the most fun to look at, so when I finally got the chance to draw my own comic strip, I knew I wanted to make the Sunday *Calvin and Hobbes* something special.

It took me a little while to learn to use the larger Sunday space effectively. It requires a somewhat different pace for the humor, and, of course, a big color panel is no place to find out that you don't know how to draw the back of your character's head. The Sunday strip shows off both strengths and weaknesses.

Occasionally I would see that an idea I'd written for a Sunday strip was not as substantial as I'd hoped it would be, and I'd realize that some of the panels and dialogue weren't adding anything significant to the story. If that were the case, I'd remove everything extraneous and use the trimmed idea for a daily strip instead. I held the Sundays to a different standard: any idea for the Sunday strip had to need the extra space. I felt a Sunday strip should do something that was impossible the rest of the week.

Over the years, I learned that daily strips are better suited for certain kinds of ideas, while Sunday strips are better for others. The daily strip is quick and to the point, perfect for a simple observation, or a short exchange between characters. Daily strips are also better for long stories, where a certain suspense can be fostered by continuing the story day after day, and the reader can remember what happened previously.

Extended conversations with real back and forth dialogue, however, don't work very well in four tiny panels—the dialogue balloons crowd out the drawings and the strip loses its grace. In a Sunday strip, you can spread out, and let the characters yap a bit. This is often funny in itself, and it's a wonderful way to let the characters' personalities emerge. It also lets you explore a topic a bit more fully.

You can talk about things without reducing them to one-liners right away.

And, of course, in today's minuscule comics, if an idea requires any real drawing, the Sunday strip is the only possible place for it. Likewise, any complex storytelling problem—a strip illustrating a long expanse of time, for example, or an event depicted in a succession of very tiny moments—is futile in the daily format. Calvin's fantasies generally migrated to the Sunday page for this reason.

In short, the Sunday page offered unique opportunities, and I deliberately tried to come up with ideas that could take advantage of them.

I usually wrote the Sunday strips separately from the dailies. For the daily strips, I tried to write an entire month's worth of ideas before inking any of them. This allowed a long period for editing and rewriting. I was less able to do this for the Sunday strips because the Sundays need to be drawn weeks further in advance and because the strips took so much longer to draw. If at all possible, however, I would try to keep two or three Sunday ideas ahead of the deadlines. I always wanted to reserve the option of abandoning an idea that didn't stand up to a few weeks of scrutiny.

For those who are interested in technical matters, the early strips were drawn on any cheap pad of Bristol board the local art supply store happened to stock. The paper was usually rather thin and sometimes the sheet wouldn't accept the ink consistently (bad sizing or something), which would make drawing aggravating and time consuming. Eventually I switched to heavier Strathmore Bristol board, which was much nicer. I used a 2H pencil to rough in the drawing, and then inked with a small sable brush and India ink. I did as little pencil work as possible in order to keep the inking more spontaneous, although the more elaborate panels required more preliminary drawing. For lettering, I used a Rapidograph cartridge pen. I drew the dialogue balloons and a few odds and ends with a crow quill pen. To cover up unwanted marks, I used various brands of Wite-Out, and in the early days, typewriter correction fluid. (Remember typewriters?) No doubt this stuff will eat through the paper or turn green in a few years, but as the original cartoons were intended for reproduction, not picture frames and gallery walls, I did not overly concern myself with archival issues or, for that matter, neatness. At some point along the way, however, I did ask the syndicate to send the printers a quality reproduction of the Sunday cartoon, rather than the original drawing, in order to reduce the amount of tape, registration marks, and general crunchings and manglings to which the drawings had previously been subjected.

Coloring the strips was a slow and tedious process. My syndicate gave me a printed sheet showing

numbered squares of color, each a mixture of various percentages of red, yellow, and blue. Using this sheet as a guide, I taped some tracing paper over the finished cartoon, and painted watercolor approximations of the available colors in the areas I wanted. This would give me a very rough idea of what the newspaper version might look like. Then I numbered each little spot of color. As the Sunday strips became more visually complex, and as I started to use color more deliberately for effects, this process became a real chore. These days, I believe much of it can be done with a few clicks of a mouse.

Colors take on different characteristics when placed next to other colors (a neutral-seeming gray might look greenish and dark next to one color, but brownish and pale in relation to another). Because of this, I came up with one little trick for coloring the strip. I cut out each of the color squares provided by the printer, so I had a stack of colors (like paint chips), rather than a sheet. By laying out the cut squares and physically placing one color next to the others I expected to use, I could see exactly how each color behaved in that particular context. As I got better at this, I was able to choose appropriate "palettes" for each strip, and create moods with color. One strip might call for contrasting, bright colors; another strip might be done with a limited group of soft, warm colors; another idea might call for a close range of grays and darks, and so on. If I made Calvin's skin a dull pink-gray to suggest dim lighting at night, I would have to find a dull yellow-gray that would suggest his hair in the same light. These challenges took an inordinate amount of time for work on deadline, but I was often quite proud of the results. A comic strip should always be fun to look at, and good use of color can contribute to that appeal. More than that, color creates its own emotional impact, which can make the drawing more expressive.

The half-page Sunday format required certain guaranteed panel divisions. The strip had to be drawn in three rows of equal height, and there was one unmovable panel division within each row. This allowed editors to reduce and reconfigure the strip to suit their particular space needs. The same strip could run in several shapes by restacking the panels.

Editors commonly removed the entire top row altogether, so in essence, a third of the strip had to be wasted on "throwaway panels" that many readers would never see. The fixed panel divisions were also annoying because they limited my ability to compose the strip to best suit the idea. For example, they often forced a small panel where I needed more space for words.

Of course, a big part of cartooning is learning to work effectively within tight space constraints. Much of cartooning's power comes from its ability to do more with less: when the drawings and ideas are

distilled to their essences, the result can be more beautiful and powerful for having eliminated the clutter. That said, there is a point at which simplification thwarts good storytelling. You can't condense *Moby Dick* into a paragraph and get the same effect. Over the years, my frustration increased and I became convinced that I could draw a better comic strip than the current newspaper format was permitting. Looking at examples of comics from the 1930s, when a Sunday strip could fill an entire page, I was amazed by the long-forgotten possibilities out there.

I took a sabbatical after resolving a long and emotionally draining fight to prevent *Calvin and Hobbes* from being merchandised. Looking for a way to rekindle my enthusiasm for the duration of a new contract term, I proposed a redesigned Sunday format that would permit more panel flexibility. To my surprise and delight, Universal responded with an offer to market the strip as an unbreakable half page (more space than I'd dared to ask for), despite the expected resistance of editors.

To this day, my syndicate assures me that some editors liked the new format, appreciated the difference, and were happy to run the larger strip, but I think it's fair to say that this was not the most common reaction. The syndicate had warned me to prepare for numerous cancellations of the Sunday feature, but after a few weeks of dealing with howling, purple-faced editors, the syndicate suggested that papers could reduce the strip to the size tabloid newspapers used for their smaller sheets of paper. Another strip could then run vertically down the side. Consequently, while some papers, primarily in larger markets, ran the strip as a half page, other papers reduced it. In some of the latter papers (including the one I read at the time), I actually lost ground: the new Sunday strip was printed even smaller than before. I was in no mood to take on new fights, so I focused on the bright side: I had complete freedom of design and there were virtually no cancellations.

For all the yelling and screaming by outraged editors, I remain convinced that the larger Sunday strip gave newspapers a better product and made the comics section more fun for readers. Comics are a visual medium. A strip with a lot of drawing can be exciting and add some variety. Proud as I am that I was able to draw a larger strip, I don't expect to see it happen again any time soon. In the newspaper business, space is money, and I suspect most editors would still say that the difference is not worth the cost. Sadly, the situation is a vicious circle: because there's no room for better artwork, the comics are simply drawn; because they're simply drawn, why should they have more room?

Business controversies aside, the new format opened up new ways to tell stories, and I drew different

kinds of strips as a result. I could write and draw the strip exactly as I imagined it, so it truly challenged my abilities. Whereas Sunday strips had previously taken me a full day to draw and color, a complex strip would now take me well into a second day to finish. Deadlines discourage this kind of indulgence, and I had to steal that extra time from what would have been some semblance of an ordinary life, but I was thrilled to expand the strip's world.

Laying out the panels became a job in itself, now that I was no longer confined to horizontal rows. I could place boxes anywhere and any size, but the reader's eye needs to flow naturally to the proper panels without confusion, and big panels need to be designed in such a way that they don't divert attention and spoil surprises. The graphic needs of each panel must be accommodated and the panels themselves should form a pleasing arrangement so the entire page is attractive, balanced, and unified as well. Here again I looked for guidance in the gorgeous Sunday pages of George Herriman's *Krazy Kat*.

The new Sunday format necessitated a change in the format of my book collections as well. Having won a bigger strip in newspapers, I wanted the book reproductions to reflect the strip's new impact as much as possible by printing the Sunday strips large. This resulted in the rather awkward horizontal format of my later books. They stick out of bookshelves, but the strips look nice. From this point on, the Sunday strips were reproduced in color with each collection, not just in the "treasury" collections, as before. (Here's a piece of trivia: because of the timing of the book format change, the cartoons from the *Snow Goons* collection were never put in a treasury book, so those Sunday strips have been reprinted only in black-and-white.)

Ten years after starting *Calvin and Hobbes*, I ended the strip. As much as I knew I'd miss the characters, the decision was long anticipated on my part. Professionally, I had accomplished far more than I'd ever set out to do and there were no more mountains I wanted to climb. Creatively, my interests were shifting away from cartooning toward painting, where I could develop my drawing skills further. And personally, I wanted to restore some balance to my life. I had given the strip all my time and energy for a decade (and was happy to do so), but now I was that much older and I wanted to work at a more thoughtful pace, out of the limelight, and without the pressures and restrictions of newspapers.

The final *Calvin and Hobbes* strip was a Sunday strip. The deadline for Sunday strips being early, I drew it well before writing the daily strips that would eventually precede it in the newspaper. I very much wanted to hit the right note for this final strip. I think it worked, but it was a bittersweet strip to draw.

Since *Calvin and Hobbes*, I've been teaching myself how to paint, and trying to learn something about music. I have no background in either subject, and there are certainly days when I wonder what made me trade proficiency and understanding in one field for clumsiness and ignorance in these others. On better days, I enjoy having so many new challenges and surprises. Even so, these new endeavors have only deepened my appreciation for comics. I no longer take quite so much for granted the versatility of comics and their ability to depict complex ideas in a beautiful, accessible, and entertaining form. For all their seeming simplicity, the expressive possibilities of comics rival those of any other art form. Five years after *Calvin and Hobbes*, I love the comics as much as ever.

Bill Watterson
Summer 2001

CALVIN AND HOBBES
SUNDAY PAGES 1985-1995

DECEMBER 29, 1985

I drew this about a month into the strip, when *Calvin and Hobbes* appeared in a few dozen newspapers. My own newspaper didn't carry the strip, which made my job feel very abstract.

The first two panels, composing the entire top row, are the "throwaway" panels that many newspapers would eliminate to make the strip smaller. Knowing that few readers would see it, I often wasted most of the space up there, but here I've drawn a nice little series of Calvin carrying on. The lower panels are all the same size. This was not an

aesthetic decision; I really didn't know what else to do. Fortunately, lack of drawing ability is rarely a liability in cartooning, and this arrangement, while unimaginative, is nevertheless effective in its simplicity and clarity. Also notice that, in a single strip, we learn something about the personality of all three characters. From the beginning, *Calvin and Hobbes* was more about characters than jokes, and I think this was an important reason the strip was able to attract an audience and survive the tough first years.

MARCH 23, 1986

This was drawn when President Reagan was staring down the Soviet Union with an arms buildup. It all seems very long ago now … thank heavens.
On the original drawing, you can see that the word “okay” has been whited out and changed to “OK,” making the little bulge at the end of the balloon unnecessary. The syndicate apparently felt that OK was more correct than okay. Eventually I learned to write it that way myself and save the syndicate some trouble.

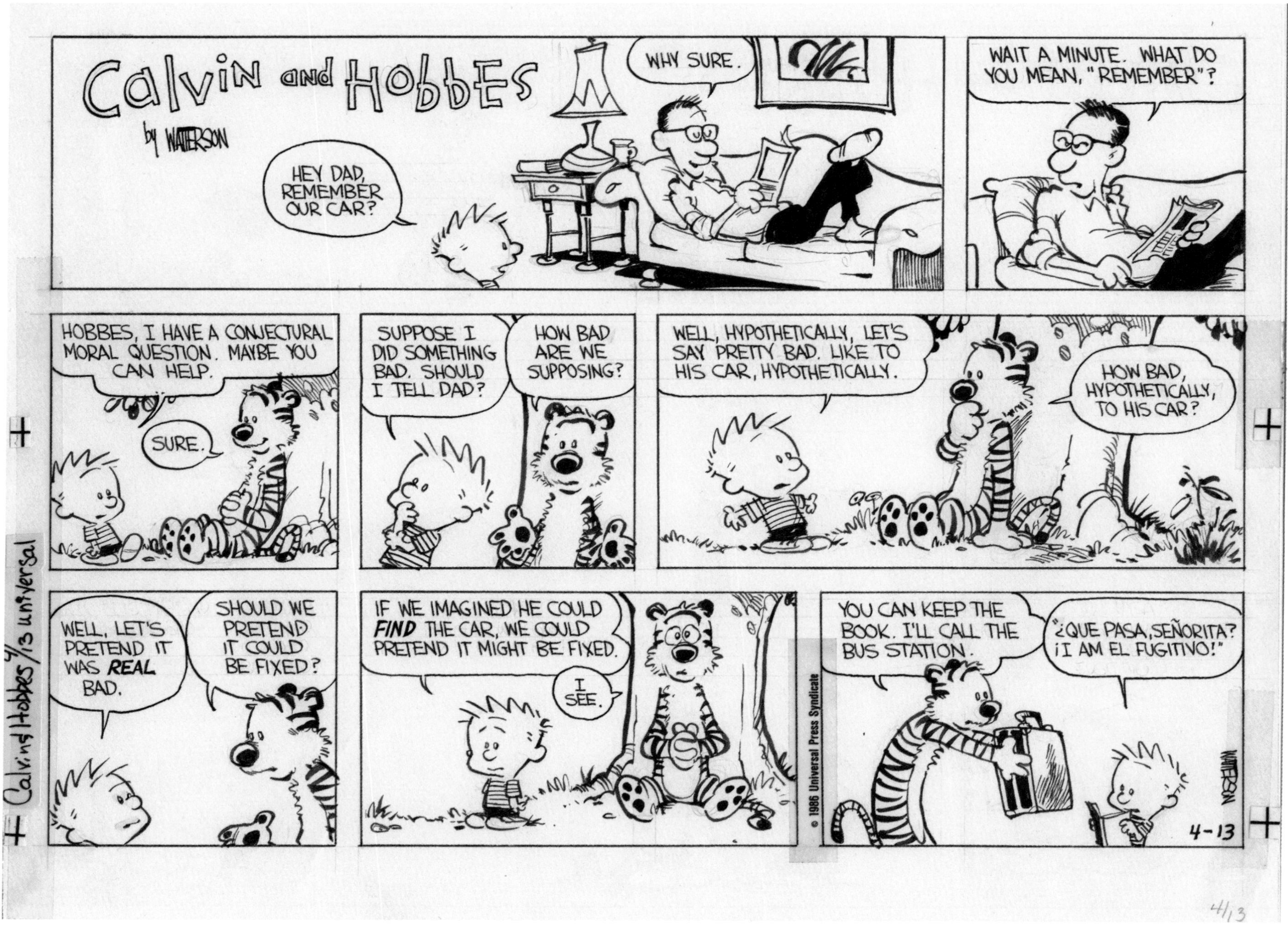

April 13, 1986

Note the pads on Hobbes's hands. I liked those as reminders that his hands were really paws, but I soon decided that the black circles were visually disruptive, and prevented the hands from being read and understood instantly. The pads stayed on Hobbes's feet, but hands are too expressive to clutter up.

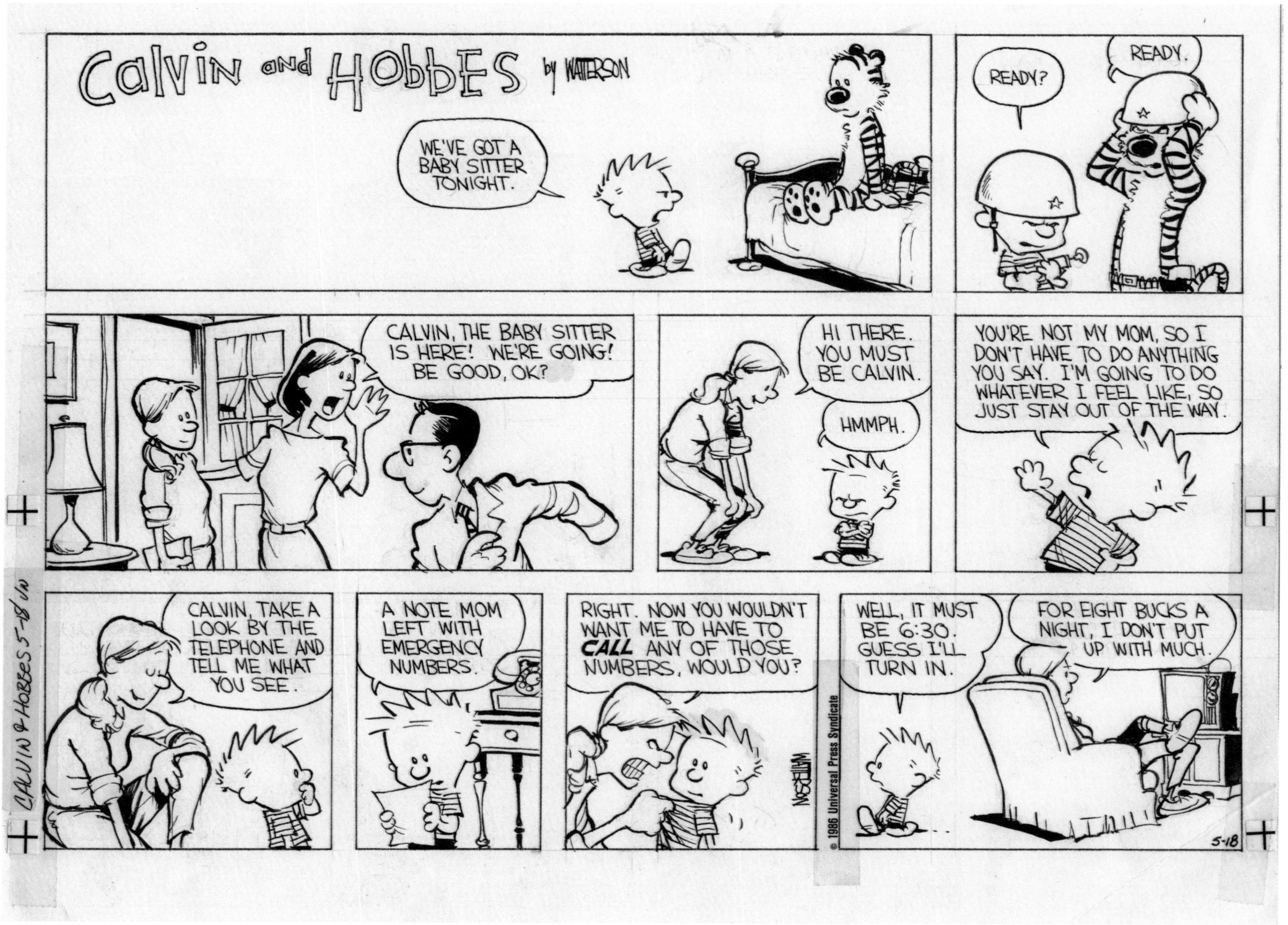

MAY 18, 1986

This was the introduction of Calvin's babysitter, Roz. She doesn't even have a name here, as I never expected to use her again. Her ferocious personality surprised me though, so she came back several times.

At that point, I used her for longer stories, continuing across daily strips, where the conflicts could play out on a larger scale.

Notice the rotary telephone and the television with UHF and VHF channel knobs. These were outdated even in 1986, but I think they're funnier looking, and have more personality, than the new ones. I think my parents were the last people in America to watch a black-and-white TV, so old appliances fit the strip that way, too.

FEBRUARY 1, 1987

Calvin and Hobbes doesn't seem that long ago, but here we are with an LP in the first panel. The drawings from this strip were often ripped off for illegal T-shirts and the like.

I wanted a page of drawings that flowed into each other, but you can see the gaps (in the middle of the second row and at left in the third row) where panel divisions were mandated. By this time, the characters were becoming more physically three-dimensional in my mind, and I had fun animating them.

FEBRUARY 15, 1987

This is one of the rare Sunday strips where the pictures don't do much of the work. A purely verbal strip is tolerable once in a while for variety, but boy, the writing had better be working hard.

Calvin and Hobbes
by WATTERSON
THE DREADED SCUM BEINGS FIRE! SPACEMAN SPIFF IS HIT!

IT NEVER FAILS. I JUST WASHED AND WAXED THIS THING.

OUR HERO, THE INTREPID SPACEMAN SPIFF, STRUGGLES WITH THE CONTROLS OF HIS DAMAGED SPACECRAFT!

THE FREEM PROPULSION BLASTERS ARE USELESS! SPIFF CRASHES ONTO THE SURFACE OF AN ALIEN PLANET!

UNSCATHED, THE FEARLESS SPACE EXPLORER EMERGES FROM THE SMOLDERING WRECKAGE! HE IS MAROONED ON A HOSTILE WORLD!

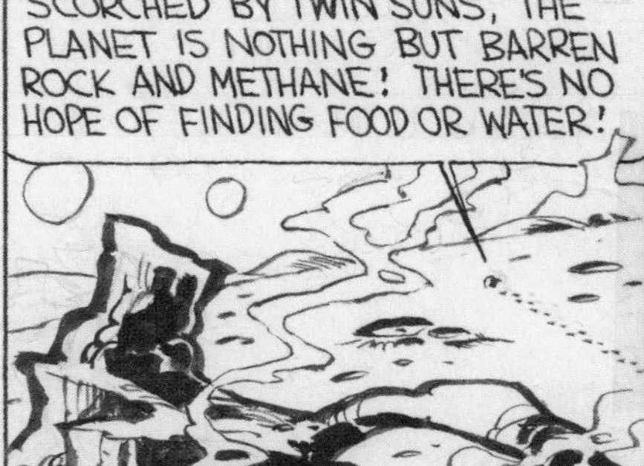
SCORCHED BY TWIN SUNS, THE PLANET IS NOTHING BUT BARREN ROCK AND METHANE! THERE'S NO HOPE OF FINDING FOOD OR WATER!

SPIFF COLLAPSES! OH NO, A HIDEOUS ALIEN SPOTS HIM! IN HIS WEAKENED STATE, SPIFF IS NO MATCH FOR THE MONSTER! THIS COULD BE THE END!!
7-5 WATTERSON
Calvin & H. 7/5 universal

LUNCHTIME! I BROUGHT YOU A SANDWICH AND SOME LEMONADE.
© 1987 Universal Press Syndicate

BRING THE DISHES BACK WHEN YOU'RE DONE, OK?

...OH WELL.
THANKS, MOM.

lunchtime.

JULY 5, 1987

CALVIN and HOBBES
by WATTERSON
THE DREADED SCUM BEINGS FIRE! SPACEMAN SPIFF IS HIT!

IT NEVER FAILS. I JUST WASHED AND WAXED THIS THING.

OUR HERO, THE INTREPID SPACEMAN SPIFF, STRUGGLES WITH THE CONTROLS OF HIS DAMAGED SPACECRAFT!

THE FREEM PROPULSION BLASTERS ARE USELESS! SPIFF CRASHES ONTO THE SURFACE OF AN ALIEN PLANET!

UNSCATHED, THE FEARLESS SPACE EXPLORER EMERGES FROM THE SMOLDERING WRECKAGE! HE IS MAROONED ON A HOSTILE WORLD!

SCORCHED BY TWIN SUNS, THE PLANET IS NOTHING BUT BARREN ROCK AND METHANE! THERE'S NO HOPE OF FINDING FOOD OR WATER!

SPIFF COLLAPSES! OH NO, A HIDEOUS ALIEN SPOTS HIM! IN HIS WEAKENED STATE, SPIFF IS NO MATCH FOR THE MONSTER! THIS COULD BE THE END!!
7-5 WATTERSON

LUNCHTIME! I BROUGHT YOU A SANDWICH AND SOME LEMONADE.
© 1987 Universal Press Syndicate

BRING THE DISHES BACK WHEN YOU'RE DONE, OK?

...OH WELL.
THANKS, MOM.

The Spaceman Spiff episodes were always fun to draw. I never really took the stories anywhere, but I loved drawing the landscapes, monsters, and spaceships. The landscape here is invented and rather generic, but in later strips, southern Utah became a great inspiration. The long throwaway panel at the top shows the type of scale and atmosphere one can evoke with a bit more room. Remove it, as many papers did, and the strip looks much more static and restrained.

SEPTEMBER 27, 1987

This strip was part of a story that was continuing across the daily strips. The daily strips were sold separately from the Sunday strips, and newspapers did not always buy both. Consequently, readers might be seeing the whole story, all of the story except this strip, or this strip and none of the story. Thus, the challenge for me was to make this strip integral to the plot, yet entirely self-sufficient, yet utterly expendable. I believe I succeeded, although I'm hard-pressed to say why I bothered.

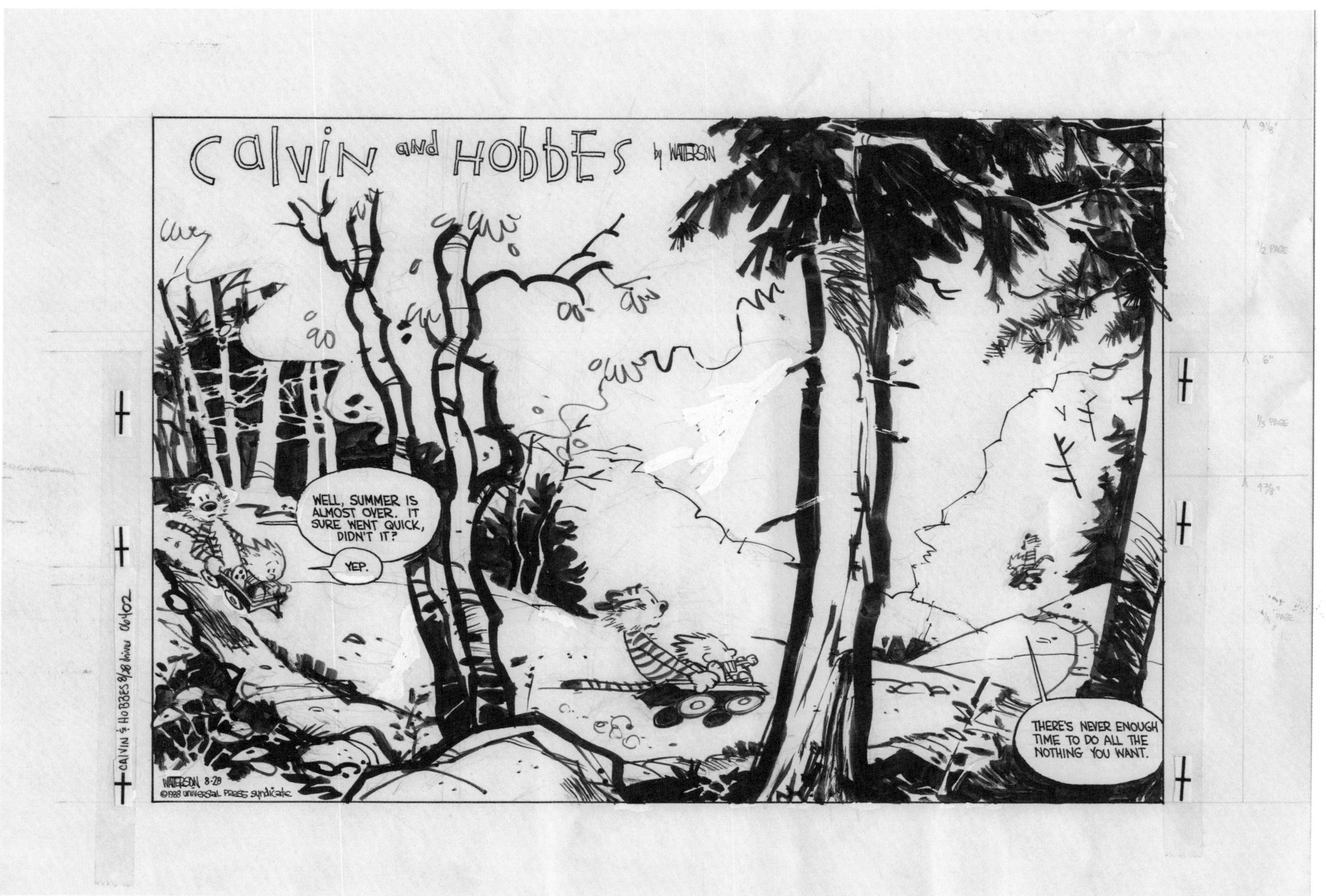

AUGUST 28, 1988

I liked the idea in this strip enough to put it in a Sunday strip, but it's very simple and I didn't want to pad it with the number of panels the usual format required. To draw the strip as one large panel, I had to condense all the words and action at the very bottom, so editors could hack away at the rest of the drawing if they wanted to print a smaller strip. On the edge of the original, you can see where I've marked the various page divisions. As is, the strip would run as a

half page of the newspaper. Take off the top (the "throwaway panels") and the strip would run as a third of a page. Lop off another inch and a half, and the bottom part can be printed as a quarter page. The trick was to compose the drawing so that it would look intentional no matter how it was cropped.

This strip presented a further problem when it came time to be reprinted in a book collection. The strip, no matter how it's cropped, is horizontal, but the books had either a square or vertical format. The only solution was to redraw the whole thing in a vertical format for the books.

MARCH 26, 1989

Several of my favorite Sunday strips depict an entire day. It's a slightly different way of telling the story, as there is no real plot. Instead, numerous isolated moments are illustrated, and the connection between them is largely made in hindsight. The Sunday strip offers enormous flexibility in storytelling, and this gradually attracted more and more of my interest.

Calvin and HOBBES

by WATTERSON

UH-OH. SOMETHING IS SERIOUSLY WRONG HERE.

THE LAWS OF PERSPECTIVE HAVE BEEN REPEALED!

OBJECTS NO LONGER DIMINISH IN SIZE WITH DISTANCE!

LINES DO NOT CONVERGE TOWARD ANY POINT ON THE HORIZON!

ALL SPATIAL RELATIONSHIPS ARE LOST! IT'S IMPOSSIBLE TO JUDGE WHERE ANYTHING IS! OH NO!

CALVIN, QUIT RUNNING AROUND AND CRASHING INTO THINGS, OR I'LL SELL YOU TO THE MONKEY HOUSE!

...AND NOW **SHE'S** LOST PERSPECTIVE.
WATTERSON 6-4

JUNE 4, 1989

Calvin and Hobbes

by WATTERSON

AHHHH...

UH-OH. SOMETHING IS SERIOUSLY WRONG HERE.

THE LAWS OF PERSPECTIVE HAVE BEEN REPEALED!

OBJECTS NO LONGER DIMINISH IN SIZE WITH DISTANCE!

LINES DO NOT CONVERGE TOWARD ANY POINT ON THE HORIZON!
©1989 UNIVERSAL PRESS SYNDICATE

ALL SPATIAL RELATIONSHIPS ARE LOST! IT'S IMPOSSIBLE TO JUDGE WHERE ANYTHING IS! OH NO!

CALVIN, QUIT RUNNING AROUND AND CRASHING INTO THINGS, OR I'LL SELL YOU TO THE MONKEY HOUSE!

...AND NOW SHE'S LOST PERSPECTIVE.
WATTERSON 6-4

It's surprisingly tricky to draw things exactly wrong, because you have to know the rules pretty well to break every single one. The strip was fun to draw.

JULY 9, 1989

With every strip, my goal is to surprise myself. If I'm not surprised, the reader surely won't be either. The surprises are usually fairly small, so it's a real delight when an idea pops in from Pluto. The soap opera drawing style, the ludicrous dialogue, the bizarre storyline—every part of this strip confounded

expectations. I hoped the reader would wonder for a second if *Calvin and Hobbes* had been replaced by another strip.

I wish I'd drawn this with a bit more flair in the line work. Some of the old continuity strips were very stylishly drawn and I'd like to have captured that. What I didn't know at that time was that many of those cartoonists drew very large. Doubling or tripling the size of my original would have helped.

SEPTEMBER 10, 1989

Here I was beginning to get a little more adventurous with panel layout, although I was still constrained by the mandated space divisions. The open spaces and different box shapes give the strip a looser feel. When the strip was restacked in some papers and in the book collections, the visual rhythm could go out of whack. Open panels might be next to each other, and boxed panels might all line up on the left side, and so on. The flexibility of the format always had a price.

Calvin and Hobbes
by Watterson
WAK WAK WAK WAK WAK WAK
F
GOOD DAY?
GETTING BETTER.
©1990 Universal Press Syndicate
WATTERSON 5-13

MAY 13, 1990

As I went along, I started eliminating dialogue from Sunday strips. Words are essential for certain kinds of ideas, but it is good to remember that cartoons are a visual medium, and pictures can do a great job of telling a story all by themselves.

Calvin and HOBBES
by WATTERSON

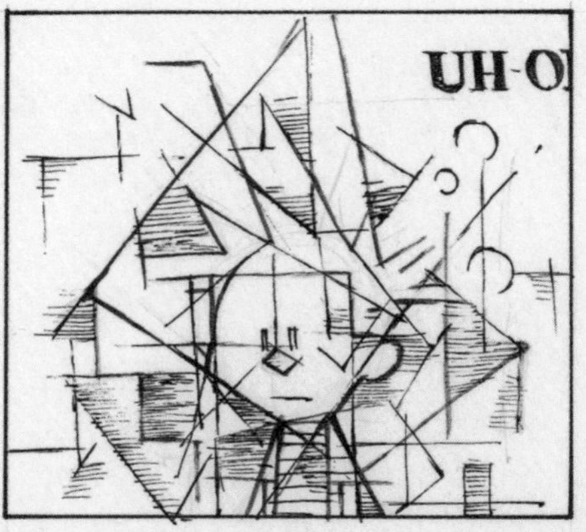
UH-O

OH NO! EVERYTHING HAS SUDDENLY TURNED NEO-CUBIST!
COMICS

IT ALL STARTED WHEN CALVIN ENGAGED HIS DAD IN A MINOR DEBATE! SOON CALVIN COULD SEE BOTH SIDES OF THE ISSUE! THEN POOR CALVIN BEGAN TO SEE BOTH SIDES OF EVERYTHING!

THE TRADITIONAL SINGLE VIEWPOINT HAS BEEN ABANDONED! PERSPECTIVE HAS BEEN FRACTURED!
©1990 Universal Press Syndicate

THE MULTIPLE VIEWS PROVIDE TOO MUCH INFORMATION! IT'S IMPOSSIBLE TO MOVE! CALVIN QUICKLY TRIES TO ELIMINATE ALL BUT ONE PERSPECTIVE!

IT WORKS! THE WORLD FALLS INTO A RECOGNIZABLE ORDER!
WATTERSON
6-17

YOU'RE STILL WRONG, DAD.

JUNE 17, 1990

Calvin and HOBBES

by WATTERSON

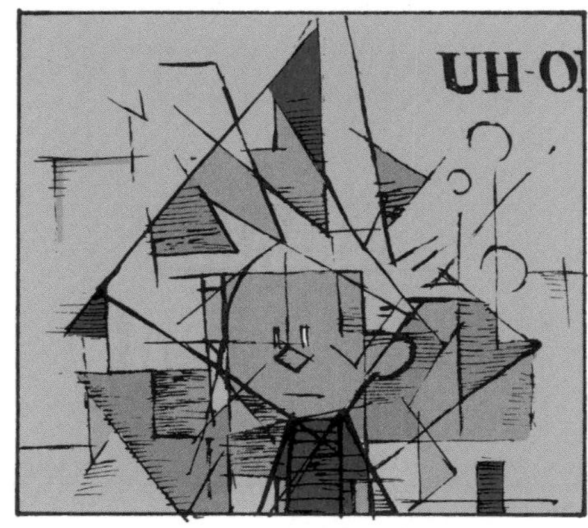

Drawing this strip required a trip to the library to see some examples of cubist art, as I'd once again written material over my own head. The idea for this strip came from my tendency to examine issues until I'm incapacitated by the persuasiveness of all sides.

Calvin and Hobbes
by Watterson

WELL! PEANUT BUTTER!

...OR SO IT SEEMS.

DID YOU SEE THAT?
HMM? WHAT?

MY SANDWICH WIGGLED! THERE'S SOMETHING ALIVE IN IT!
OH STOP IT, CALVIN.

I'M NOT KIDDING! MOM MUST BE TRYING TO KILL ME! I BET THERE'S A SLUG IN MY PEANUT BUTTER!
EWW!

HMM... I DON'T FEEL ANY SLUGS IN HERE. WHAT COULD IT BE? I'D BETTER SMELL IT.

AUGH! AUGH! IT'S GOT MY NOSE!! THE PEANUT BUTTER ITSELF IS ALIVE!

IT'S OOZING UP MY FACE! IT'S GOING TO SUCK OUT MY EYEBALLS! HELP!

RRGH! MMF! BLRGHGH!

©1990 UNIVERSAL PRESS SYNDICATE
I GOT IT OFF! QUICK! DROWN IT IN CHOCOLATE MILK!

BOY, WHAT A CLOSE CALL THAT WAS! WON'T MOM BE DISAPPOINTED TO SEE HER LITTLE PLOT FAILED!
LOOK AT YOU! I'VE NEVER SEEN ANYTHING SO REVOLTING! WHAT'S WRONG WITH YOU?!

I'M EATING SOMEWHERE ELSE.
9·16

GIRLS ARE SO WEIRD.
WATTERSON

SEPTEMBER 16, 1990

Calvin and Hobbes

by Watterson

WELL! PEANUT BUTTER!

...OR SO IT SEEMS.

DID YOU SEE THAT?
HMM? WHAT?

MY SANDWICH WIGGLED! THERE'S SOMETHING ALIVE IN IT!
OH STOP IT, CALVIN.

I'M NOT KIDDING! MOM MUST BE TRYING TO KILL ME! I BET THERE'S A SLUG IN MY PEANUT BUTTER!
EWW!

HMM... I DON'T FEEL ANY SLUGS IN HERE. WHAT COULD IT BE? I'D BETTER SMELL IT.

AUGH! AUGH! IT'S GOT MY NOSE!! THE PEANUT BUTTER ITSELF IS ALIVE!

IT'S OOZING UP MY FACE! IT'S GOING TO SUCK OUT MY EYEBALLS! HELP!

RRGH! MMF!
BLRGHGH!

I GOT IT OFF! QUICK! DROWN IT IN CHOCOLATE MILK!

BOY, WHAT A CLOSE CALL THAT WAS! WON'T MOM BE DISAPPOINTED TO SEE HER LITTLE PLOT FAILED!
LOOK AT YOU! I'VE NEVER SEEN ANYTHING SO REVOLTING! WHAT'S WRONG WITH YOU?!

I'M EATING SOMEWHERE ELSE.
9-16

GIRLS ARE SO WEIRD.
WATTERSON

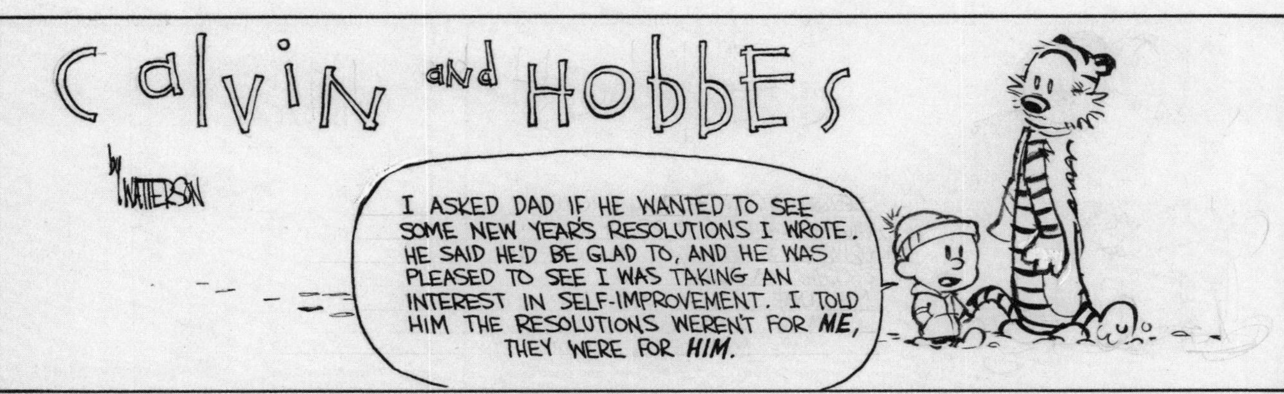

December 30, 1990

Calvin and HOBBES

by WATTERSON

I ASKED DAD IF HE WANTED TO SEE SOME NEW YEAR'S RESOLUTIONS I WROTE. HE SAID HE'D BE GLAD TO, AND HE WAS PLEASED TO SEE I WAS TAKING AN INTEREST IN SELF-IMPROVEMENT. I TOLD HIM THE RESOLUTIONS WEREN'T FOR ME, THEY WERE FOR HIM.

THAT'S WHY WE'RE OUTSIDE NOW.
I WONDERED WHAT THE RUSH WAS.

I'M GETTING DISILLUSIONED WITH THESE NEW YEARS.

THEY DON'T SEEM VERY NEW AT ALL! EACH NEW YEAR IS JUST LIKE THE OLD YEAR!

HERE ANOTHER YEAR HAS GONE BY AND EVERYTHING'S STILL THE SAME! THERE'S STILL POLLUTION AND WAR AND STUPIDITY AND GREED! THINGS HAVEN'T CHANGED!

I SAY WHAT KIND OF FUTURE IS THIS?! I THOUGHT THINGS WERE SUPPOSED TO IMPROVE! I THOUGHT THE FUTURE WAS SUPPOSED TO BE BETTER!
©1990 Universal Press Syndicate

THE PROBLEM WITH THE FUTURE IS THAT IT KEEPS TURNING INTO THE PRESENT.
WATTERSON 12-30

Calvin and Hobbes
by WATTERSON
CALVIN SUDDENLY REALIZES THE WORLD HAS NO HUE, VALUE, OR CHROMA!
HAVE THE PHOTORECEPTORS IN CALVIN'S EYES STOPPED WORKING PROPERLY, OR HAS THE FUNDAMENTAL NATURE OF LIGHT CHANGED?
PERHAPS SOME STRANGE NUCLEAR OR CHEMICAL REACTION ON THE SUN HAS CAUSED ELECTROMAGNETIC RADIATION TO DEFY SEPARATION INTO A SPECTRUM!
MAYBE OBJECTS NO LONGER REFLECT CERTAIN WAVELENGTHS! WHATEVER THE CAUSE, IT'S CLEAR TO CALVIN THAT THERE'S NO POINT IN DISCUSSING THINGS WITH HIS DAD!
© WATTERSON dist. by UNIVERSAL PRESS SYNDICATE
THE PROBLEM IS, YOU SEE EVERYTHING IN TERMS OF BLACK AND WHITE.
SOMETIMES THAT'S THE WAY THINGS ARE!!
2-3 WATTERSON

FEBRUARY 3, 1991

Unlike most art, comics often lose something in the original. In newspapers the last panel was in color. To draw this strip, I not only avoided color and halftones, I avoided outlines. As the top "throwaway"

Calvin and HOBBES
by WATTERSON

CALVIN SUDDENLY REALIZES THE WORLD HAS NO HUE, VALUE, OR CHROMA!

HAVE THE PHOTORECEPTORS IN CALVIN'S EYES STOPPED WORKING PROPERLY, OR HAS THE FUNDAMENTAL NATURE OF LIGHT CHANGED ??

PERHAPS SOME STRANGE NUCLEAR OR CHEMICAL REACTION ON THE SUN HAS CAUSED ELECTROMAGNETIC RADIATION TO DEFY SEPARATION INTO A SPECTRUM!

MAYBE OBJECTS NO LONGER REFLECT CERTAIN WAVELENGTHS! WHATEVER THE CAUSE, IT'S CLEAR TO CALVIN THAT THERE'S NO POINT IN DISCUSSING THINGS WITH HIS DAD!
© WATTERSON dist. by UNIVERSAL PRESS SYNDICATE

THE PROBLEM IS, YOU SEE EVERYTHING IN TERMS OF BLACK AND WHITE.
SOMETIMES THAT'S THE WAY THINGS ARE!!
2-3 WATTERSON

panels illustrate, the placement of black is crucial to making the pictures comprehensible.

During my fight to prevent *Calvin and Hobbes* from being turned into licensed merchandise, I was accused of having a black-and-white view of the issue. The arguing dragged on for years and was very frustrating and unpleasant, so it was a bit of a release to get an interesting strip idea out of the conflict.

April 19, 1992

This strip was done in the new half–page format. It has only six panels, but I think the space is used attractively.

To an editor, space may be money, but to a cartoonist, space is time. Space provides the tempo and rhythm of the strip. Used well, it directs the eye to speed up or linger. The long drawing of Hobbes walking away is a sort of visual brake. It's empty, so the eye rests there and the panel creates a pause.

MAY 24, 1992

Although conservative in panel layout, I could now use the entire space without threat of having panels removed or rearranged for different newspaper formats. Readers would finally see everything I drew, exactly the way I drew it.

There are lots of words in this strip. That's always somewhat visually oppressive, but the dialogue has some spirit and I think there's enough going on to reward the reader's patience. The color helped enliven the drawings too. I'd have used more black if this were intended to remain uncolored.

I usually saved the G.R.O.S.S. strips for longer stories in the dailies, but the new space in the Sundays was an irresistible opportunity to let the characters bounce off each other for a while.

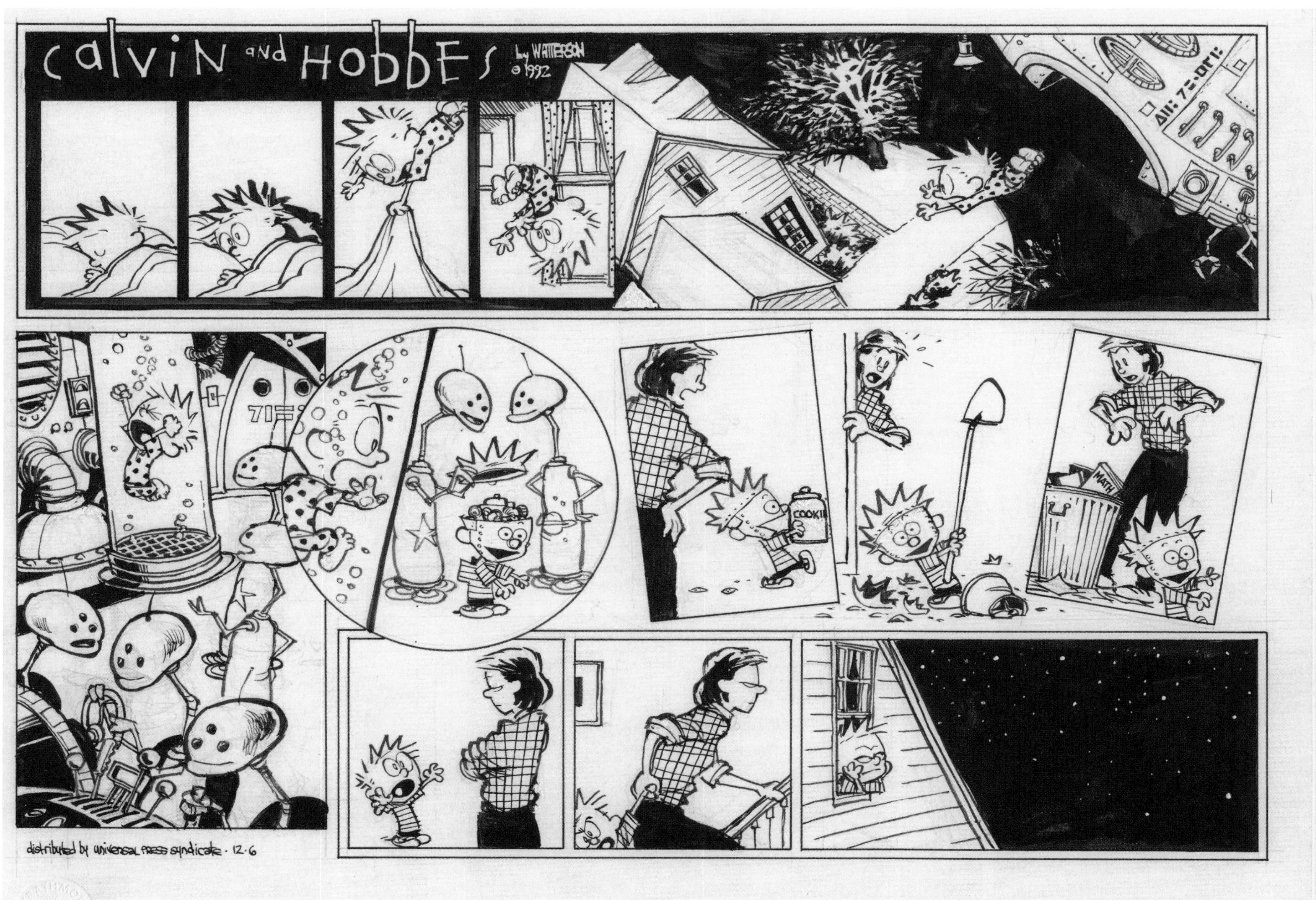

DECEMBER 6, 1992

I think much of the fun in this strip comes from the details in the drawing. The visual richness encourages you to look at the strip for a moment even after you get the joke. This pleasure is largely lost now that newspapers print the comics so small.

DECEMBER 13, 1992

With the large Sundays, I felt that *Calvin and Hobbes* kicked into high gear. The large format not only encouraged new ways of presenting ideas, it forced me to push the drawings, to make Calvin's world as bold and energetic as I could. I felt the strip finally looked the way it did in my head.

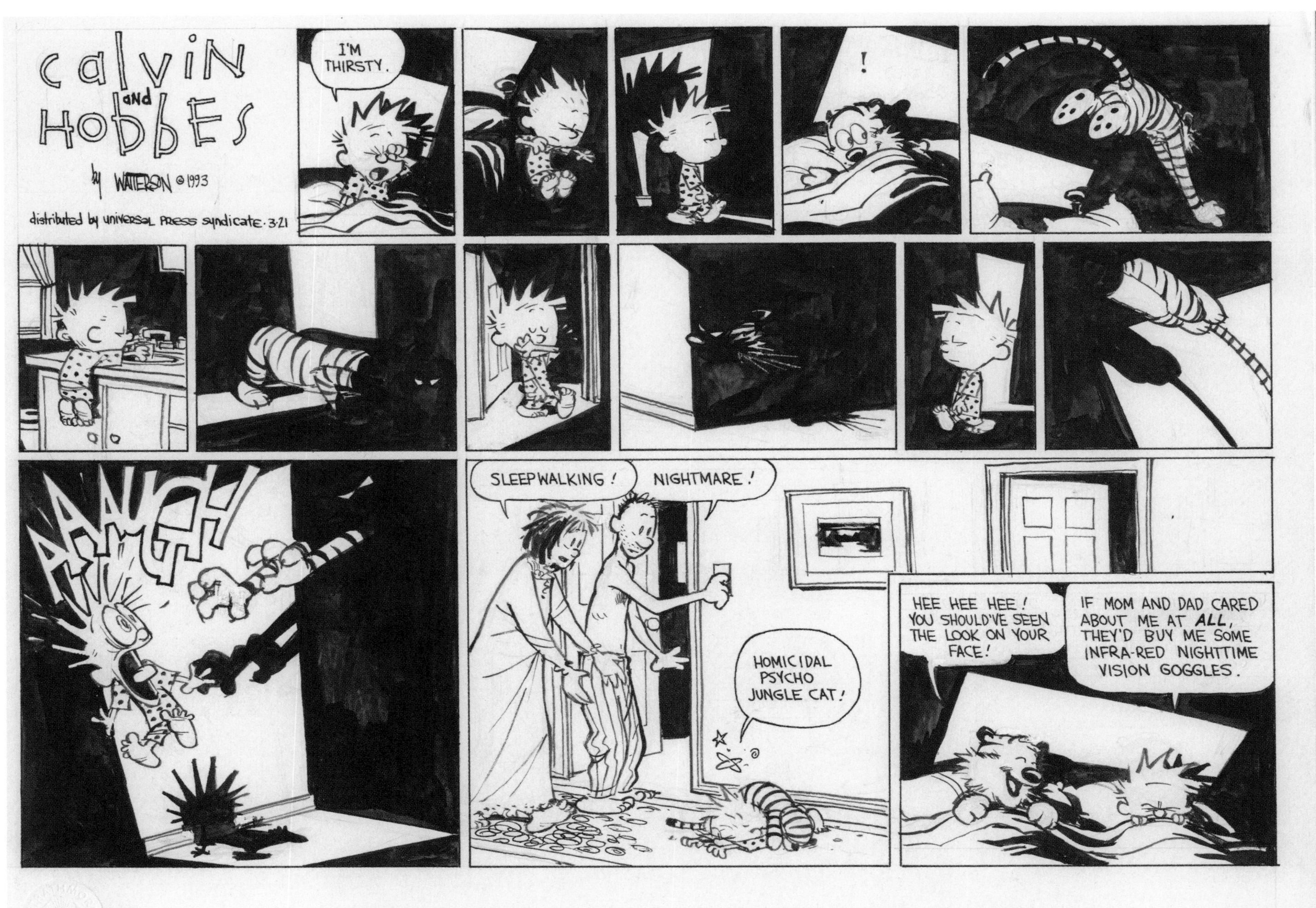

MARCH 21, 1993

I can't read this strip without thinking of the cat who inspired much of Hobbes's personality. Sprite was an exuberant gray tabby we had. Enlarge her to tiger size, and this is what things would be like. The last panel drawing looks just like her.

This strip gave me my favorite book title.

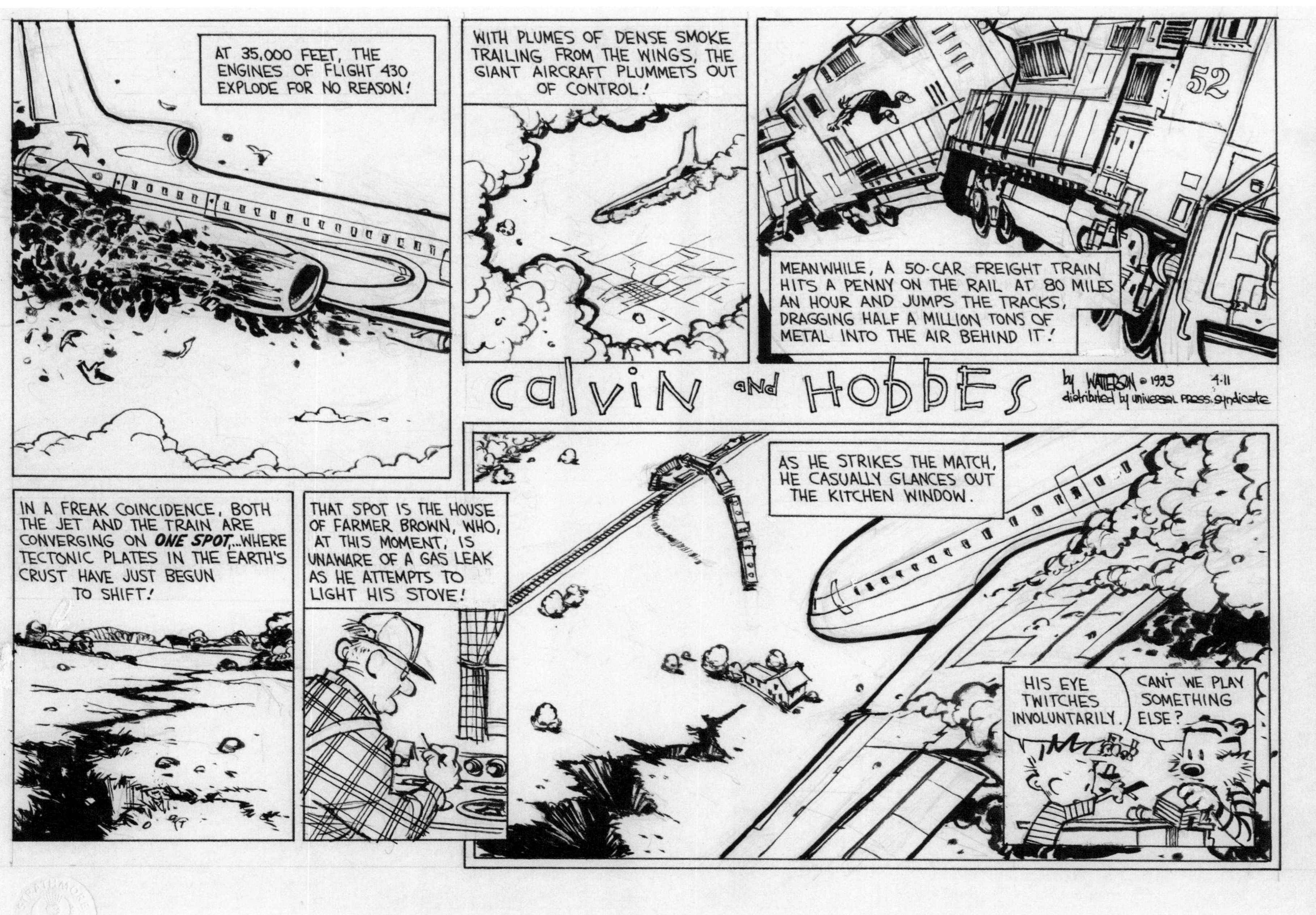

APRIL 11, 1993

AT 35,000 FEET, THE ENGINES OF FLIGHT 430 EXPLODE FOR NO REASON!

WITH PLUMES OF DENSE SMOKE TRAILING FROM THE WINGS, THE GIANT AIRCRAFT PLUMMETS OUT OF CONTROL!

52
MEANWHILE, A 50-CAR FREIGHT TRAIN HITS A PENNY ON THE RAIL AT 80 MILES AN HOUR AND JUMPS THE TRACKS, DRAGGING HALF A MILLION TONS OF METAL INTO THE AIR BEHIND IT!

calvin and HOBBES

by WATTERSON © 1993 4-11
distributed by universal press syndicate

IN A FREAK COINCIDENCE, BOTH THE JET AND THE TRAIN ARE CONVERGING ON ***ONE SPOT***...WHERE TECTONIC PLATES IN THE EARTH'S CRUST HAVE JUST BEGUN TO SHIFT!

THAT SPOT IS THE HOUSE OF FARMER BROWN, WHO, AT THIS MOMENT, IS UNAWARE OF A GAS LEAK AS HE ATTEMPTS TO LIGHT HIS STOVE!

AS HE STRIKES THE MATCH, HE CASUALLY GLANCES OUT THE KITCHEN WINDOW.
HIS EYE TWITCHES INVOLUNTARILY.
CAN'T WE PLAY SOMETHING ELSE?

Calvin and Hobbes
by WATTERSON ©1993 dist. by universal press syndicate 7·4
GAS
WEED KILLER
CALVIN, I SPENT OVER AN HOUR FIXING THIS! AT LEAST TRY IT!
I SAW WHAT WENT IN IT! I'M NOT TOUCHING IT!

JULY 4, 1993

I like the little touches in these drawings—the octopus legs trailing out of the fridge, the use of a plumber's helper as a cooking utensil, the notion that shrunken heads might be sold in jars, etc. As you might guess, I was an unappreciative little kid once.

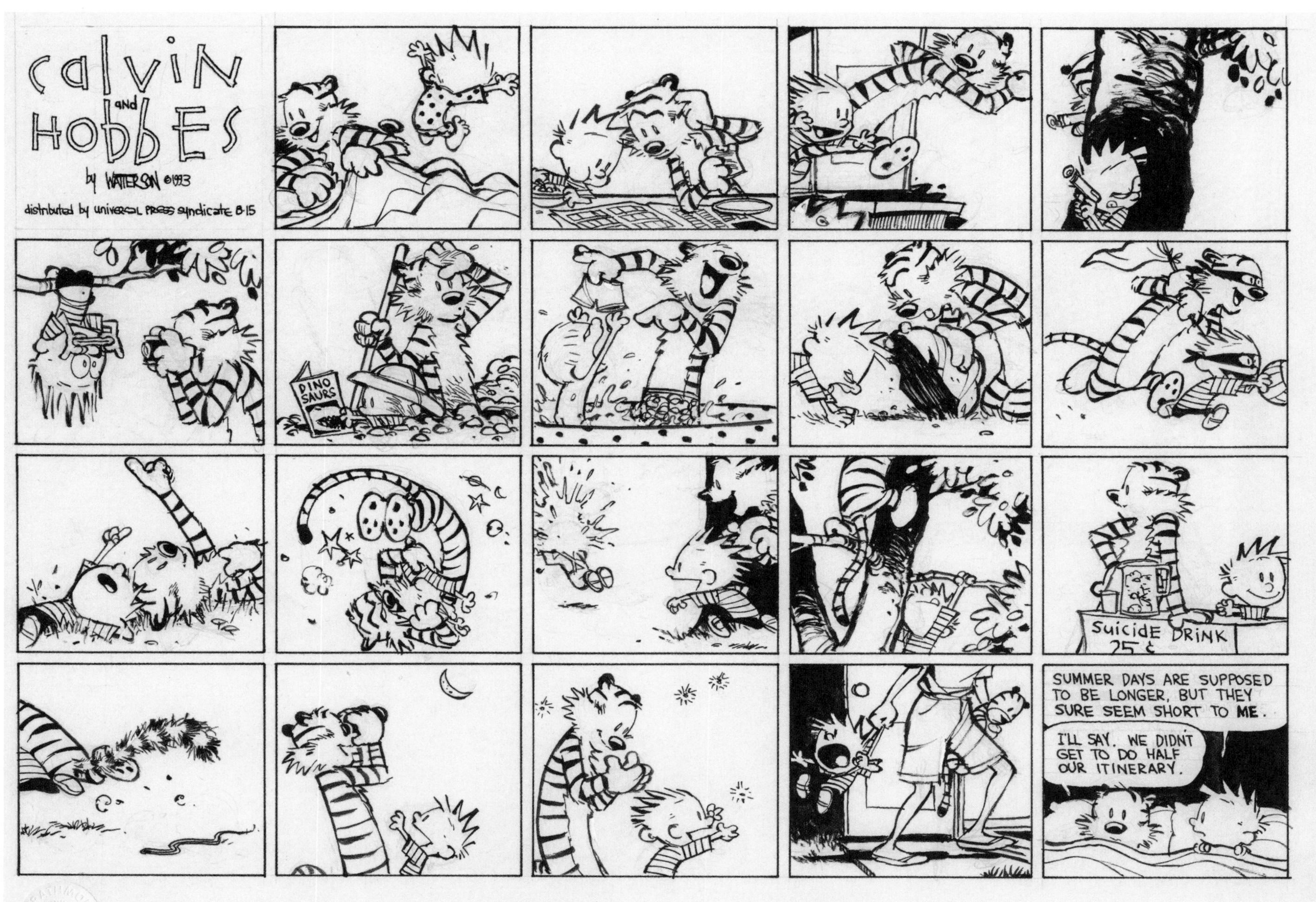

AUGUST 15, 1993

Count 'em: nineteen panels. You can draw a big, fat summer day in nineteen panels. This strip would have a very different feel with less space.

NOVEMBER 7, 1993

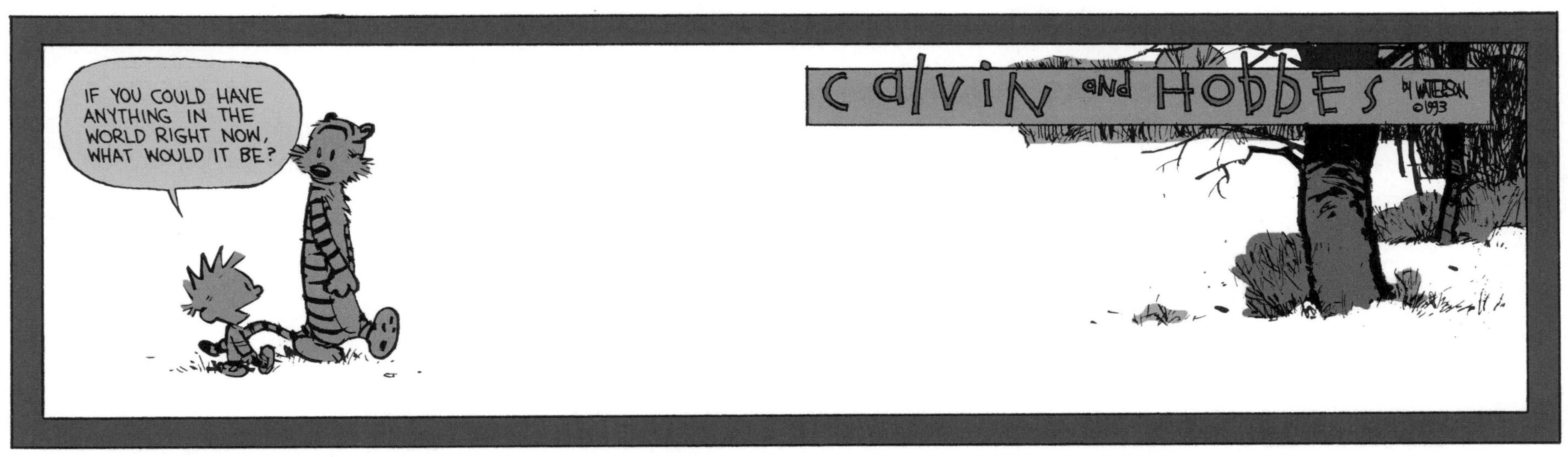

I sometimes tried for the spare visual effect of a Japanese print—very few things, but precisely placed. In November strips, I always tried to capture that austere, gray, brambly look that Ohio gets.

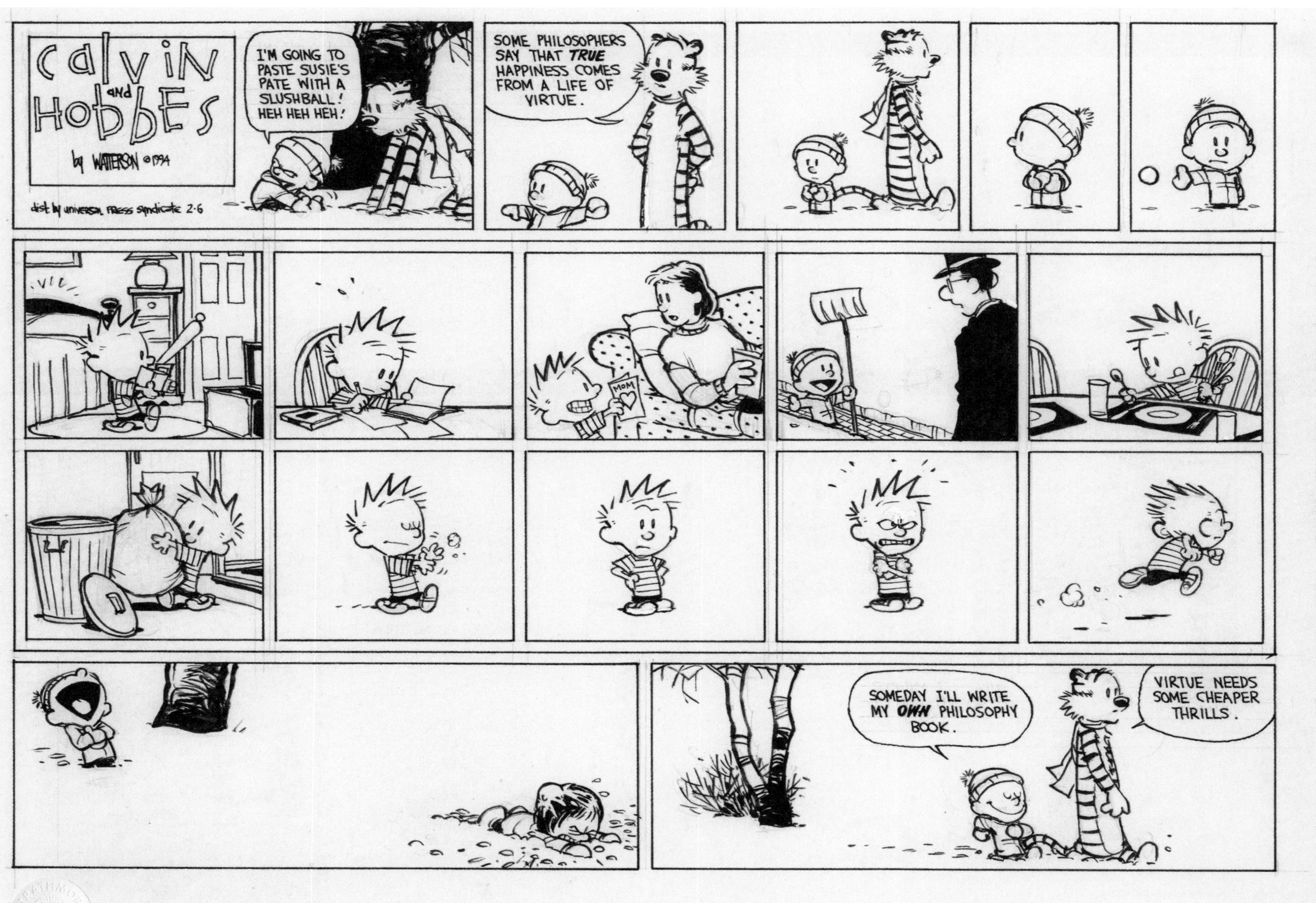

FEBRUARY 6, 1994

The choice between good and evil was a recurring theme in the strip, and nothing tested Calvin like a good slushball.

Calvin and Hobbes
by WATTERSON ©1994
dist. by universal press syndicate 3-6
BLECCHHH
"TO BE ?? ..OR.. NOT TO BE? *SIGHHH* THAT IS THE QUESTION.
WHETHER 'TIS NOBLER IN THE MIND TO SUFFER THE SLINGS AND ARROWS OF OUTRAGEOUS FORTUNE...
...OR TO TAKE ARMS AGAINST A SEA OF TROUBLES... AND BY OPPOSING, END THEM?
THWUPP
TO DIE: TO SLEEP; .. NO MORE!
AND BY A SLEEP TO SAY WE END THE HEARTACHE AND THE THOUSAND NATURAL SHOCKS THAT FLESH IS HEIR TO...
SNIFF 'TIS A CONSUMMATION DEVOUTLY TO BE WISHED.'
TO DIE, TO SLEEP!
TO SLEEP, PERCHANCE TO DREAM: AY, THERE'S THE RUB!
.. FOR IN THAT SLEEP OF DEATH, WHAT DREAMS MAY COME WHEN WE HAVE SHUFFLED OFF THIS MORTAL COIL MUST GIVE US PAUSE."
Blink Blink
FEEHEELINGGS
WO WO WO
YOU FINISHED THAT RIGHT UP! DID YOU LIKE IT?
LET'S NOT HAVE THIS EVER AGAIN.

MARCH 6, 1994

This is one of the weirdest strips I drew, and I'm not exactly sure I understand it myself, but it still makes me laugh, so there you are.

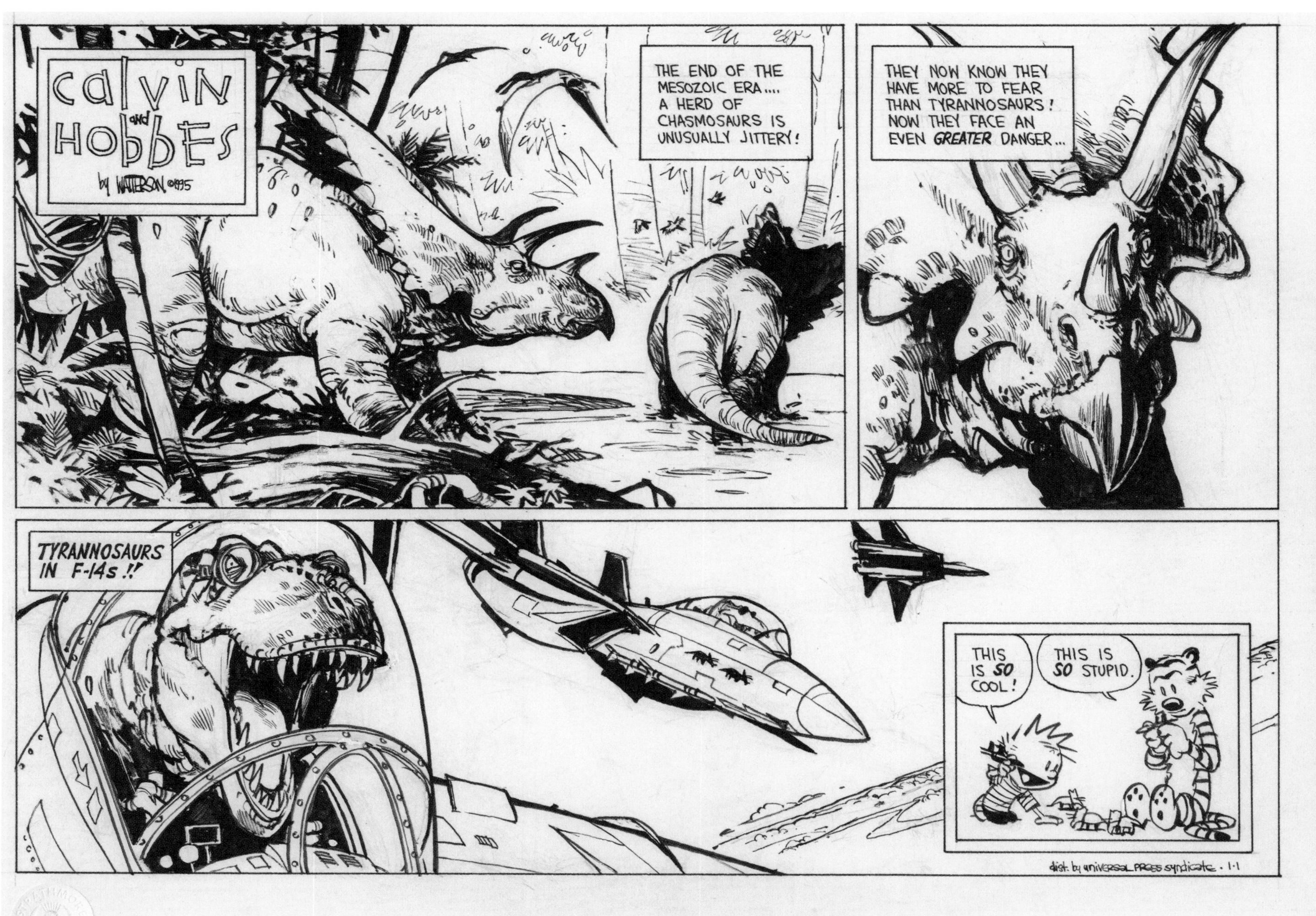

JANUARY 1, 1995

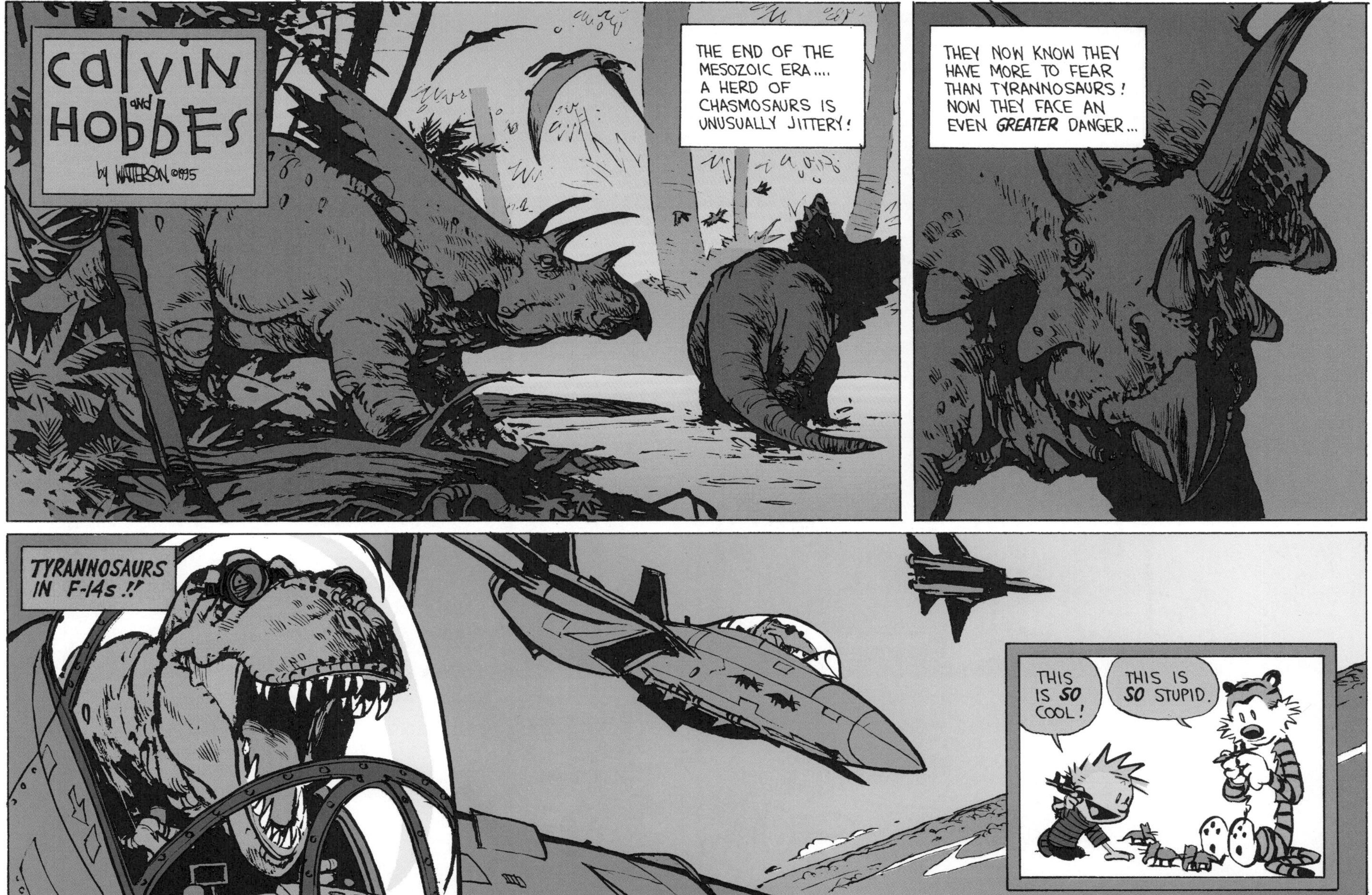

The dinosaur strips always took forever to draw, since I had to imagine and construct them from skeleton diagrams and other illustrations. They were a lot of fun if the deadlines weren't right on top of me. This one was a little tricky, because the T. Rex anatomy doesn't fit easily into an airplane cockpit, and it required a little fudging.

Calvin and Hobbes
by WATTERSON ©1995
dist. by universal press syndicate · 5·14
Show and Tell
YOU KNOW, HOBBES, SOME DAYS EVEN MY LUCKY ROCKETSHIP UNDERPANTS DON'T HELP.
WELL, YOU'VE DONE ALL YOU CAN DO.

MAY 14, 1995

Calvin and Hobbes

by WATTERSON ©1995
dist. by universal press syndicate · 5.14

If I had any extra room to spare, I'd try to make the panel design interesting. Here the large black rectangle visually separates Calvin's school day from his time at home. The crooked panels and heavy use of black are tricks I learned from *Krazy Kat*. This sort of design can be distracting and annoying if not handled with restraint. The panels can be interesting, but they should never divert attention from the drawings.

WE ALL WANT MEANINGFUL LIVES. WE LOOK FOR MEANING IN EVERYTHING WE DO.
BUT SUPPOSE THERE IS NO MEANING! SUPPOSE LIFE IS FUNDAMENTALLY ABSURD!
SUPPOSE THERE'S NO REASON, OR TRUTH, OR RIGHTNESS IN ANYTHING!
Calvin and HOBBES
by WATTERSON ©1995 dist. by universal PRESS syndicate
7-30
WHAT IF NOTHING MEANS ANYTHING? WHAT IF NOTHING REALLY MATTERS?
I GUESS THERE'S NO HARM IN A LITTLE WISHFUL THINKING.
OR SUPPOSE EVERYTHING MATTERS. WHICH WOULD BE WORSE??

JULY 30, 1995

Whenever the strip got ponderous, I put Calvin and Hobbes in their wagon and sent them over a cliff. It had a nice way of undercutting the serious subjects, and it often doubled as a visual metaphor as well. Plus, it's a lot more fun to draw than a series of talking heads.

SEPTEMBER 24, 1995

This strip has a lot of back and forth conversation, and the idea was to create a sense of escalating lunacy. Once again, you can't do this sort of thing in just a few panels. Nor would this work across several daily strips—you'd lose the momentum. The large Sunday format captured the spirit of *Calvin and Hobbes* in ways that had been impossible before.

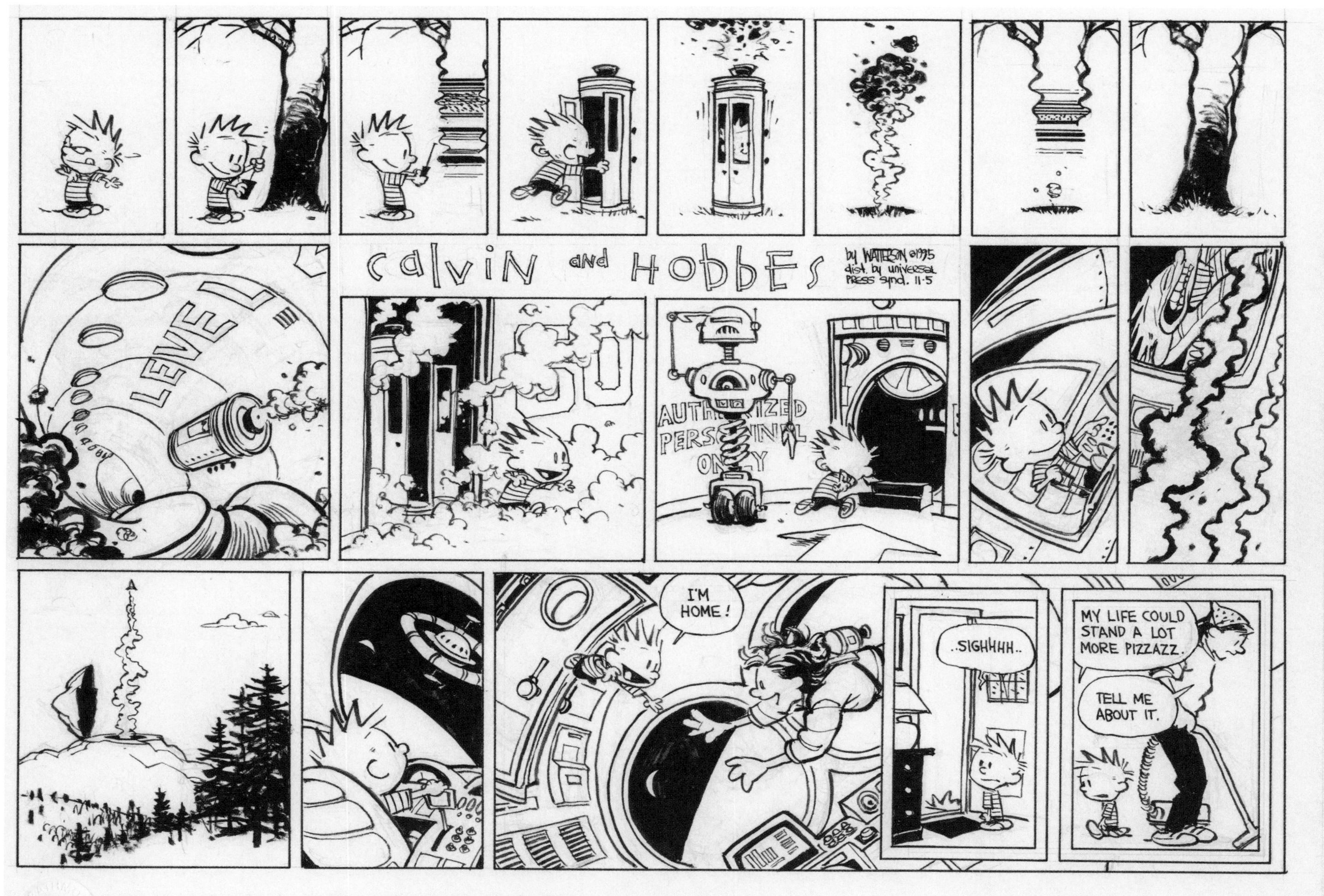

NOVEMBER 5, 1995

LEVEL
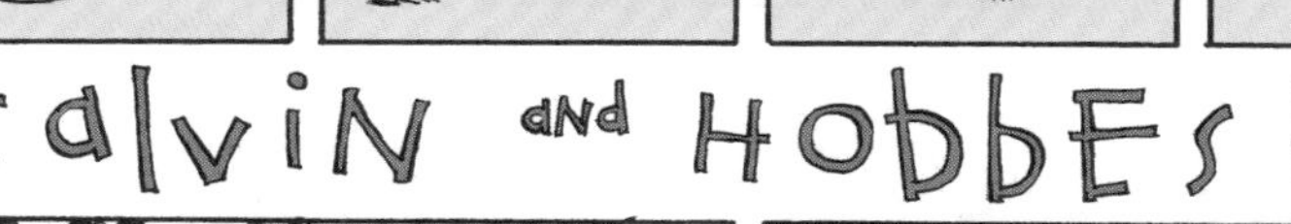
calvin and HOBBES
by WATTERSON ©1995
dist. by universal
PRESS synd. 11-5

I'M HOME!

..SIGHHHH..

MY LIFE COULD STAND A LOT MORE PIZZAZZ.
TELL ME ABOUT IT.

NOVEMBER 19, 1995

Another strip with no words at all. I kept the panel design extremely clean and simple, so nothing gets in the way of the frantic story. I'm very pleased with how each moment is distilled. A lot of experience fed into each picture by this point.

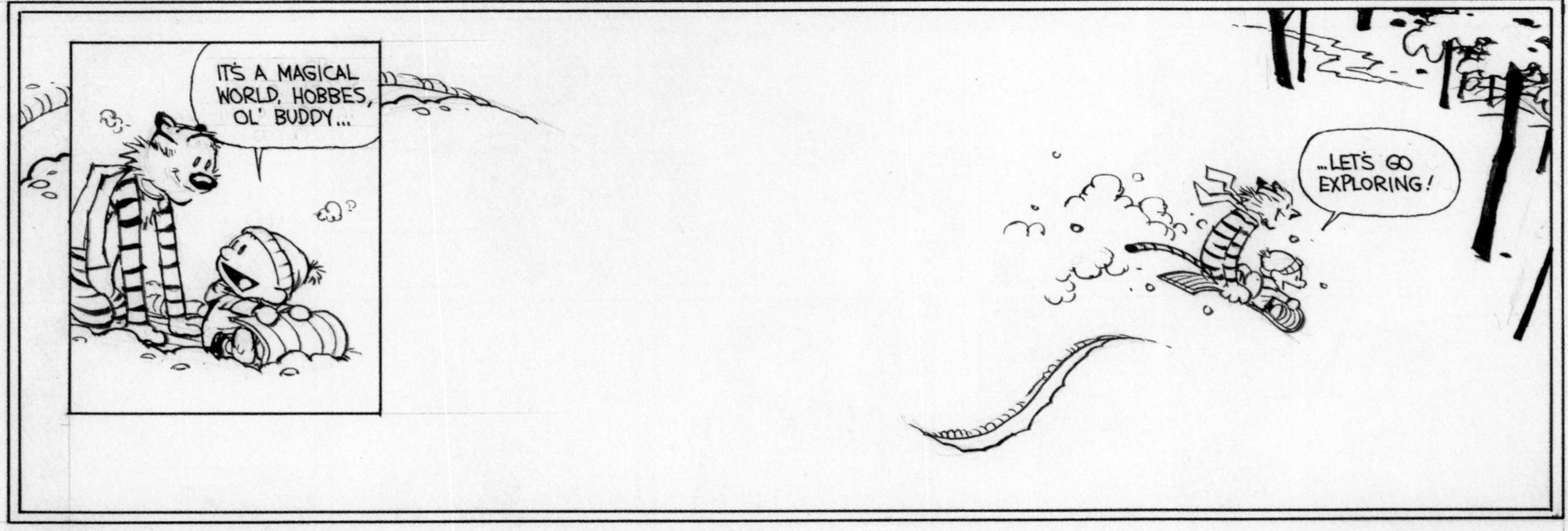

DECEMBER 31, 1995

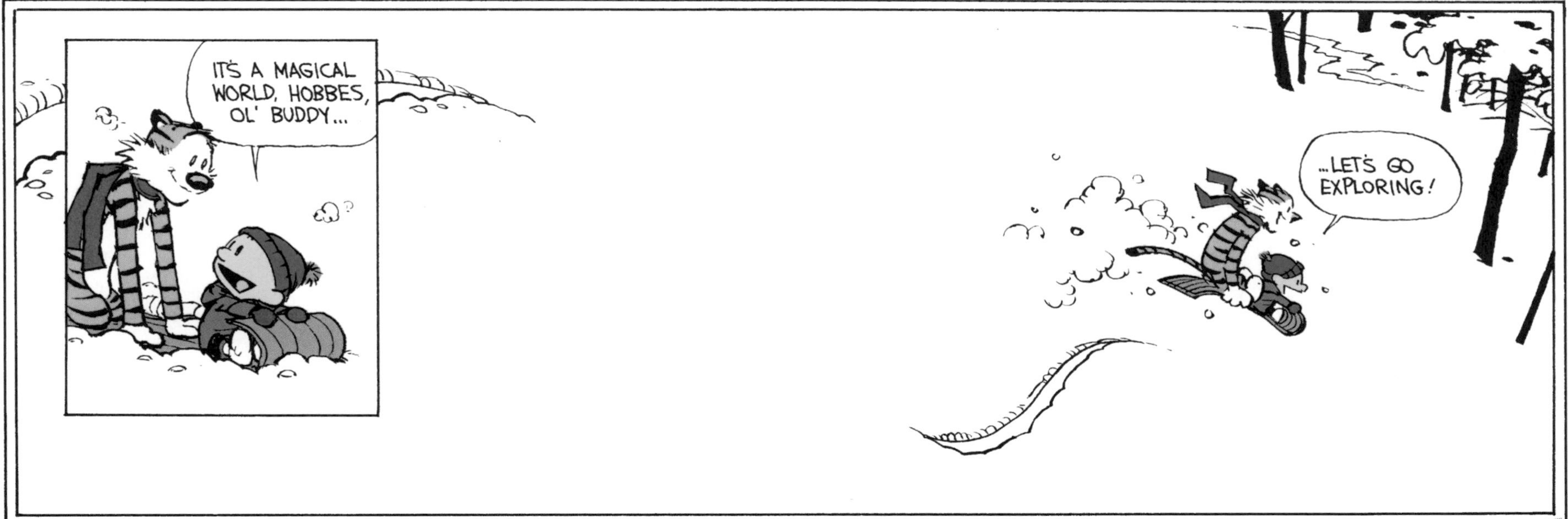

This was the final strip of *Calvin and Hobbes*. I typically colored panel borders and word balloons, but in this strip, I left everything white. Only the characters and the sled were colored, so the drawing would have a very spare and open look to mirror the ideas in the dialogue.

SELECTED BIBLIOGRAPHY

Calvin and Hobbes comic strips by Bill Watterson were collected and reprinted in the following volumes, all of which were published by Andrews McMeel Publishing:

Calvin and Hobbes. 1987.
Something Under the Bed Is Drooling. 1988.
The Essential Calvin and Hobbes. 1988.
Yukon Ho! 1989.
The Calvin and Hobbes Lazy Sunday Book. 1989.
Weirdos from Another Planet! 1990.
The Authoritative Calvin and Hobbes. 1990.
Scientific Progress Goes "Boink." 1991.
The Revenge of the Baby-Sat. 1991.
The Indispensable Calvin and Hobbes. 1992.
Attack of the Deranged Mutant Killer Monster Snow Goons. 1992.
The Days Are Just Packed. 1993.
Homicidal Psycho Jungle Cat. 1994.
The Calvin and Hobbes Tenth Anniversary Book. 1995.
There's Treasure Everywhere. 1996.
It's a Magical World. 1996.

Additional information about Bill Watterson and his work may be found in the following:

Richard Marschall. "Oh, You Kid: A Strip of Leviathan Quality, *The Comics Journal* 127 (February 1989), 72-77.
Bill Watterson. "Calvin and Hobbes," *CARTOONIST PROfiles* 68 (December 1985), 36-41.
———. "Some Thoughts on *Pogo* and Comic Strips Today," *CARTOONIST PROfiles* 80 (December 1988), 12-19.
———. "The Cheapening of the Comics," *The Comics Journal* 137 (September 1990), 93-98.
Richard Samuel West. "Interview: Bill Watterson," *The Comics Journal* 127 (February 1989), 56-71.
———. "Errors and Misconceptions," *The Comics Journal* 130 (July 1989), 52.

More Praise for th
and Mathem

"'This is the greatest assignment ever!' He more than enough to know that I had a mathematics. Thanks for putting this great program together, we LOVE IT!"

—Jeff Thompson, Walt Morey Middle School,
Troutdale, Oregon

"The Fantasy Sports and Mathematics programs allow you to reach the students, making the lessons not only comprehensive and enriching, but very exciting. The students loved it, worked harder than ever, and their GEPA scores increased over 40 points in the first year alone!"

—Robert Creamer, Woodbine School District,
Woodbine, New Jersey

"Fantasy Football and Mathematics *is a great resource! My students have never been so excited about a unit. I even have former students participating in it on their own!"*

—Jason Williams, Azalea Middle School,
St. Petersburg, Florida

"The beauty of the Fantasy Sports and Mathematics programs is that while all the students are busy having fun, enjoying the competition, and building better relationships with sports-minded parents, they are, much to their surprise, learning to love math."

—Ryan D. Verver, Southwest Chicago Christian School,
Tinley Park, Illinois

"Playing Fantasy Football and Mathematics *from a preservice teacher perspective allows my secondary math methods students to see the power of teaching math with motivational and mathematically sound materials. My students are very engaged in fantasy football."*

—Dana Pomykal Franz, assistant professor,
curriculum and instruction, Mississippi State University

"Students were eager to be the first in their math class to tally their scores and begin working with their team's stats. It was great to see boys and girls who were working both above and below grade level fully engaged in using their math skills and learning new ones."

—Sara Suchman, Harvard Graduate School of Education,
former middle school director

"Fantasy Sports and Mathematics! Finally, a fun and effective method not only for teaching math knowledge but also for going further and providing a framework for students to comprehend, apply, and analyze the learned competencies. A rare and innovative example of academics using sports to teach students life skills."

—Kim Beason, associate professor,
park and recreation management, University of Mississippi

"Fantasy Football and Mathematics *is becoming a sixth-grade tradition! The students are really enjoying it. We devote every Wednesday to it, and on the week where there was no school on Wednesday you would have thought the world was going to end!"*

—Jennifer Rising, mathematics chair,
Tuxedo Park School, Tuxedo, New York

"Fantasy Football and Mathematics *is a user-friendly curriculum that teaches essential basic skills in an exciting format, which reaches students of all levels."*

—Nicole Lyman, Garber High School, Essexville, Michigan

"I've never seen kids so excited about math before. The competition among students has resulted in them not even realizing the amount of mathematics involved. Thank you!"

—Dee Shober, North Warren Middle School,
Blairstown, New Jersey

"As a high school math lab special education teacher, I have found Fantasy Football easily adaptable to meet the needs of all the different academic skill levels in my class."

—Debbie Stewart-Karsmarski, Bulkeley High School,
Hartford, Connecticut

"Dan Flockhart's innovative Fantasy Sports and Mathematics books are rich and innovative tools for inspiring students to delve deeply into the study of mathematics."

—Ann Diver-Stamnes, professor, School of Education,
Humboldt State University, California

Jossey-Bass Teacher

Jossey-Bass Teacher provides K–12 teachers with essential knowledge and tools to create a positive and lifelong impact on student learning. Trusted and experienced educational mentors offer practical classroom-tested and theory-based teaching resources for improving teaching practice in a broad range of grade levels and subject areas. From one educator to another, we want to be your first source to make every day your best day in teaching. *Jossey-Bass Teacher* resources serve two types of informational needs—essential knowledge and essential tools.

Essential knowledge resources provide the foundation, strategies, and methods from which teachers may design curriculum and instruction to challenge and excite their students. Connecting theory to practice, essential knowledge books rely on a solid research base and time-tested methods, offering the best ideas and guidance from many of the most experienced and well-respected experts in the field.

Essential tools save teachers time and effort by offering proven, ready-to-use materials for in-class use. Our publications include activities, assessments, exercises, instruments, games, ready reference, and more. They enhance an entire course of study, a weekly lesson, or a daily plan. These essential tools provide insightful, practical, and comprehensive materials on topics that matter most to K–12 teachers.

Fantasy Football and Mathematics

Fantasy Sports and Mathematics Series

Fantasy Baseball and Mathematics: A Resource Guide for Teachers and Parents, Grades 5 and Up

Fantasy Baseball and Mathematics: Student Workbook

Fantasy Basketball and Mathematics: A Resource Guide for Teachers and Parents, Grades 5 and Up

Fantasy Basketball and Mathematics: Student Workbook

Fantasy Football and Mathematics: A Resource Guide for Teachers and Parents, Grades 5 and Up

Fantasy Football and Mathematics: Student Workbook

Fantasy Soccer and Mathematics: A Resource Guide for Teachers and Parents, Grades 5 and Up

Fantasy Soccer and Mathematics: Student Workbook

Fantasy Football and Mathematics

A Resource Guide for Teachers and Parents

Dan Flockhart

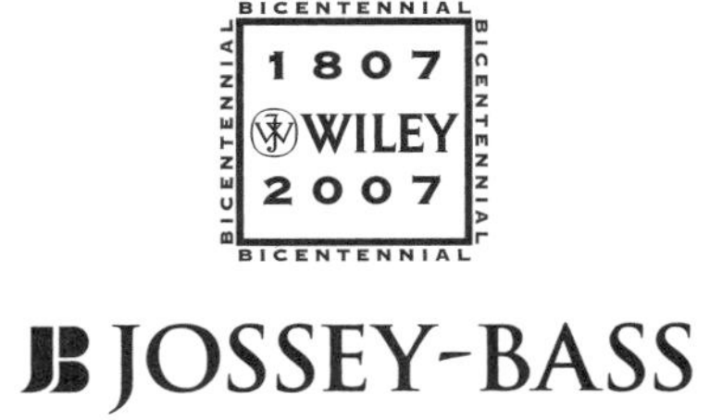

JOSSEY-BASS

Published by Jossey-Bass
A Wiley Imprint
989 Market Street, San Francisco, CA 94103-1741 www.josseybass.com

Jossey-Bass books and products are available through most bookstores. To contact Jossey-Bass directly call our Customer Care Department within the U.S. at 800-956-7739, outside the U.S. at 317-572-3986, or fax 317-572-4002.

Jossey-Bass also publishes its books in a variety of electronic formats. Some content that appears in print may not be available in electronic books.

ISBN: 978-0-7879-9444-0

Printed in the United States of America
FIRST EDITION
PB Printing 10 9 8 7 6 5 4 3 2 1

About This Book: FAQs

What is Fantasy Football and Mathematics?
Fantasy Football and Mathematics is a game that is played by millions of adolescents and adults nationwide. Participants create fantasy teams by selecting players or teams from high school, college, or professional football. They may also select players or teams from high school football, assuming that they have access to their statistics. The football players and teams earn points based on their performances in their games. Each week, students use newspapers or online resources to locate their players' or team statistics in order to find out how many total points their team earned. The object of the game is to accumulate the highest number of points.

How much time is required to play the game?
Students can compute their weekly points in 15 to 40 minutes.

Where can I find the players' statistics?
Players' statistics are found in box scores (summaries of games) in newspapers as well as online at www.fantasysportsmath.com and other sports Web sites.

How much preparation time will I need?
You will need very little preparation time if students use online resources to gather data or if you have access to newspapers-in-education programs, in which students can receive free newspapers.

Where can I find help?
A support forum for teachers can be found at www.fantasysportsmath.com. Teachers can enter their students in contests there as well.

How do I assess the skills that are covered?
This book contains forty-six practice worksheets and forty-six corresponding assessments in the form of quizzes. In addition, a comprehensive pretest/posttest is included.

When can I play the game?
Football season begins in early September and concludes in late December (the regular season).

About the Author

Dan Flockhart received his multiple-subject teaching credential from California State University, East Bay in 1988. He taught mathematics in grades 5 through 8 for eleven years at St. Matthew's Episcopal Day School in San Mateo, California, where he incorporated fantasy sports into his math curriculum. He has also taught general studies classes at College of the Redwoods in Eureka, California. He received a master of arts degree in education from Humboldt State University in 2005; the title of his thesis was "Teacher Perceptions of the Effects of Fantasy Football in the Teaching of Mathematics." Flockhart has enjoyed participating in fantasy sports for over twenty-five years.

In addition to authoring the Fantasy Sports and Mathematics series, Flockhart maintains a Web site, www.fantasysportsmath.com, where teachers can participate in forums and contests and find out more about the series.

To my former students at
St. Matthew's Episcopal Day School

Acknowledgments

This book would not have been possible without the help and support of several people. I thank Sara, Ann, and Cathy for their valuable input. I am also thankful to Kate, who made all of this possible. You are one of my angels! I was also lucky to work with wonderful production editors, Elizabeth and Susan, and copyeditors, Carolyn and Bev. They were fun to work with and I was impressed with their willingness to do whatever it took to produce the best possible product. My thanks go out as well to Chris for creating one of the best covers I've ever seen. In addition, I'm grateful to Lena for ensuring that all the math is accurate and Tiffany for her continual support as well as the countless hours she spent on this project. Finally, I express my gratitude to Tom, who introduced me to the game, and John, the master of the cheat sheet.

Contents

Introduction

Welcome to Fantasy Football and Mathematics, an exciting and easy-to-use program that takes advantage of the fantasy sports phenomenon. I created this educational program by combining twenty-five years of participation in fantasy sports and eleven years of experience teaching mathematics in grades 5 through 8. This curriculum was the most successful one I used in the classroom; both boys and girls ran into my room on a daily basis, wanting to play the game.

Fantasy Football and Mathematics is a game in which students select and manage teams of professional, college, or high school football players. The football players earn points based on their performances in real games. Each week, students use newspapers or online resources to locate their players' statistics in order to find out how many points were earned by their team. The goal of the game is to accumulate the highest number of points.

This comprehensive resource guide is supported by research (see www.fantasysportsmath.com). The program includes lesson plans, student handouts, graphing activities, a pretest/posttest, forty-six practice worksheets, forty-six quizzes, and more than one hundred scoring systems that give teachers and parents the flexibility to customize the content according to the skill level of the students. Fantasy Football and Mathematics addresses the social and cognitive needs of students because it is based on a pedagogy that is student-centered. Students work collaboratively in groups to compute their weekly points, check their peers' answers, and create their graphs. Students become active learners as they select their teams and starting lineups. Consequently, this autonomy helps students build their decision-making skills. Students also receive multiple exposures to concepts, facilitating mastery. Moreover, the hands-on features (technology, newspapers, and graphing activities) address all three learning styles: auditory (learning by listening), visual (learning by seeing), and kinesthetic or tactile (learning by doing and touching). These features help to meet the needs of all students and result in a high level of student interest.

Fantasy Football and Mathematics has three components. The first element is computation of weekly points. The second element consists of graphing activities, and is optional. The third component is integration of practice worksheets and corresponding quizzes into the game, which is also optional.

All players' names in this text are fabricated. However, students will select real football players. Consequently, the game is fun and dynamic. In addition, preparation time for teachers is minimal once the game has begun.

Teachers using this program can enter their students in contests at www.fantasysportsmath.com. A support forum for teachers can be found there as well. Let's get started!

National Council of Teachers of Mathematics Standards and Expectations Addressed by *Fantasy Football and Mathematics*

Portions of the standards that appear in italics are not covered. Some standard points are not included because the book does not address them.

Number and Operations Standard for Grades 3–5
Understand numbers, ways of representing numbers, relationships among numbers, and number systems:

- Understand the place-value structure of the base-ten number system and be able to represent and compare whole numbers and decimals
- Develop understanding of fractions as parts of unit wholes, as parts of a collection, as locations on number lines, and as divisions of whole numbers
- Recognize and generate equivalent forms of commonly used fractions, decimals, and percents
- Explore numbers less than 0 by extending the number line and through familiar applications

Understand meanings of operations and how they relate to one another:

- Understand the effects of multiplying and dividing whole numbers
- Understand and use properties of operations, such as the distributivity of multiplication over addition

Compute fluently and make reasonable estimates:

- Develop fluency in adding, subtracting, multiplying, and dividing whole numbers

Algebra Standard for Grades 3–5

Understand patterns, relations, and functions:

- Represent and analyze patterns and functions, using words, tables, and graphs

Represent and analyze mathematical situations and structures using algebraic symbols:

- Identify such properties as commutativity, associativity, and distributivity and use them to compute with whole numbers
- Represent the idea of a variable as an unknown quantity using a letter or a symbol
- Express mathematical relationships using equations

Measurement Standard for Grades 3–5

- Understand such attributes as length, area, weight, *volume,* and *size of angle* and select the appropriate type of unit for measuring each attribute
- Carry out simple unit conversions, such as from centimeters to meters, within a system of measurement
- Select and apply appropriate standard units and tools to measure length, area, *volume,* weight, *time, temperature,* and *the size of angles*
- Develop, understand, and use formulas to find the area of rectangles and *related triangles* and *parallelograms*

Data Analysis and Probability Standard for Grades 3–5

- Represent data using tables and graphs such as *line plots,* bar graphs, and line graphs

Select and use appropriate statistical methods to analyze data:

- Propose and justify conclusions and predictions that are based on data *and design studies to further investigate the conclusions or predictions*

Understand and apply basic concepts of probability:

- Predict the probability of outcomes of simple experiments and test the predictions
- Understand that the measure of the likelihood of an event can be represented by a number from 0 to 1

Problem Solving Standard for Grades Prekindergarten–12

- Build new mathematical knowledge through problem solving
- Solve problems that arise in mathematics and in other contexts

- Apply and adapt a variety of appropriate strategies to solve problems
- Monitor and reflect on the process of mathematical problem solving

Reasoning and Proof Standard for Grades Prekindergarten–12

- Recognize reasoning and proof as fundamental aspects of mathematics
- Make and investigate mathematical conjectures

Communication Standard for Grades Prekindergarten–12

- Organize and consolidate their mathematical thinking through communication
- Communicate their mathematical thinking coherently and clearly to peers, teachers, and others
- Use the language of mathematics to express mathematical ideas precisely

Connections Standard for Grades Prekindergarten–12

- Recognize and use connections among mathematical ideas
- Understand how mathematical ideas interconnect and build on one another to produce a coherent whole
- Recognize and apply mathematics in contexts outside of mathematics

Representation Standard for Grades Prekindergarten–12

- Create and use representations to organize, record, and communicate mathematical ideas
- Select, apply, and translate among mathematical representations to solve problems

Number and Operations Standard for Grades 6–8

Understand numbers, ways of representing numbers, relationships among numbers, and number systems:

- Work flexibly with fractions, decimals, and percents to solve problems
- Compare and order fractions, decimals, and percents efficiently and find their approximate locations on a number line
- Understand and use ratios and proportions to represent quantitative relationships
- Develop an understanding of large numbers and recognize and appropriately use exponential, scientific, and *calculator* notation
- Use factors, multiples, prime factorization, *and relatively prime numbers* to solve problems
- Develop meaning for integers and represent and compare quantities with them

Understand meanings of operations and how they relate to one another:

- Understand the meaning and effects of arithmetic operations with fractions, decimals, and integers
- Use the associative and commutative properties of addition and multiplication and the distributive property of multiplication over addition to simplify computations with integers, fractions, and decimals
- Understand and use the inverse relationships of addition and subtraction, multiplication and division, and squaring and finding square roots to simplify computations and solve problems

Compute fluently and make reasonable estimates:

- *Develop* and analyze algorithms for computing with fractions, decimals, and integers and develop fluency in their use

Algebra Standard for Grades 6–8

Understand patterns, relations, and functions:

- Develop an initial conceptual understanding of different uses of variables
- Recognize and generate equivalent forms for simple algebraic expressions and solve linear equations

Measurement Standard for Grades 6–8

Understand measurable attributes of objects and the units, systems, and processes of measurement:

- Understand both metric and customary systems of measurement
- Understand relationships among units and convert from one unit to another within the same system

Apply appropriate techniques, tools, and formulas to determine measurements:

- Select and apply techniques and tools to accurately find length, area, *volume,* and angle measures to appropriate levels of precision
- Develop and use formulas to determine the circumference of circles and the *area of triangles, parallelograms, trapezoids,* and circles and *develop strategies to find the area of more-complex shapes*
- Solve problems involving scale factors, using ratio and proportion

Data Analysis and Probability Standard for Grades 6–8

- Select, create, and use appropriate graphical representations of data, including histograms, *box plots,* and scatter plots

Number and Operations Standard for Grades 9–12

- Develop an understanding of permutations and combinations as counting techniques

Algebra Standard for Grades 9–12

Understand patterns, relations, and functions:

- Understand *relations* and functions and *select, convert flexibly among, and use various representations for them*

Represent and analyze mathematical situations and structures using algebraic symbols:

- Use symbolic algebra to represent and explain mathematical relationships

Data Analysis and Probability Standard for Grades 9–12

- Understand histograms, *parallel box plots,* and scatter plots and use them to display data

Computing Weekly Points

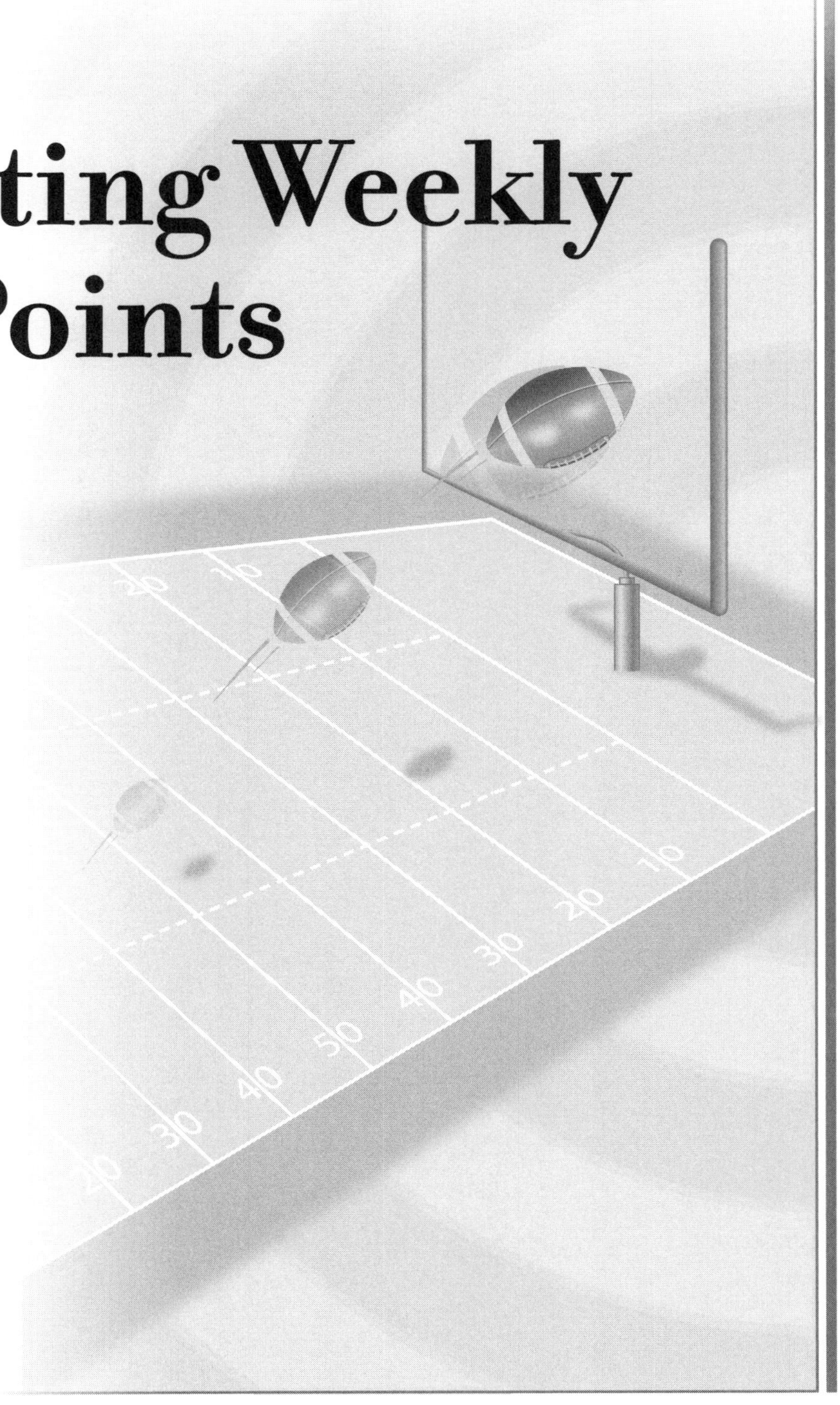

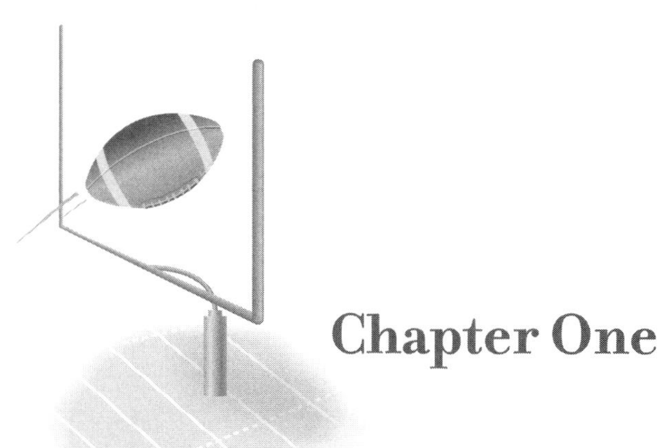

Chapter One

How to Play Fantasy Football and Mathematics

Fantasy Football and Mathematics is a game in which participants create and manage their own teams of players from actual football teams. Students can select players or teams from professional, college, or high school, provided they have access to the players' or teams' statistics. The length of high school and college football seasons is shorter than professional football. Consequently, students should not combine players from professional, college, or high school football. In other words, participants' teams will consist of professional, college, *or* high school players or teams. Football players earn points by scoring touchdowns and two-point conversions as well as accumulating passing, rushing, and receiving yards. Players lose points for interceptions thrown and fumbles lost. Each week, students find the sum of the points earned by their players, using one of the scoring systems in this book. The object of the game is to accumulate the highest number of points.

How to Play the Game
Step 1: Selecting players.
Step 2: Reading box scores.
Step 3: Collecting data.
Step 4: Computing points.

Step 1: Selecting Players

There are two options for selecting players. Option 1 includes a salary cap and player values (that is, a cost associated for each player). Player values and salary caps will be updated before each season and posted at www.fantasysportsmath.com.

The process of creating new player values is time-consuming and requires research and an extensive knowledge of players' performance over the past several years. Additional factors taken into account when assigning player values include current injuries, if players recently changed teams, the strength of defensive units in a team's division, and others. The purchase of this book entitles you to one season of free player values. Lists of player values for subsequent seasons will be provided for a nominal fee. To access player values, visit www.fantasysportsmath.com. Click on "Player Values." Type in your password, which is w8c9e3c4. This password can be used one time only, after which time it will expire.

In option 2, you avoid the salary cap and player values, but students do not receive several benefits of these critical components of the game, which are explained later.

Option 1: Permanent Teams with Salary Cap

Students have $40 million to spend on player values. Students select eleven players and two team defenses. Students may select the same players and team defenses. Table 1.1 lists the number of players selected at each position and the number in a starting lineup.

You can choose if students have to set their starting lineups before the weekend's games or if they can use the statistics from the best-performing players for that week. For example, a student could compute the points for both of her quarterbacks, then select the quarterback who generated the most points that week. I used the first method because it was less time consuming.

Table 1.1. Complete Roster and Starting Lineup Each Week

Position	Number of Players Selected for Position	Number of Players Selected for Starting Lineup
Quarterback	2	1
Running back	3	2
Wide receiver (includes tight ends)	4	3
Kicker	2	1
Team defense	2	1

The main advantage of using option 1 is that it promotes equality in the game. If students spend close to their complete salary cap, the quality of the teams should be relatively equal within the class. I had many students (both girls and boys) who knew very little about football yet managed to do very well; several even won the game. Another advantage of this option is that students have to compromise as they select players because the salary cap is structured so that they cannot simply select the top players at each position. This allows them to hone their decision-making skills, which facilitates their cognitive development. Students can also make trades.

Another benefit of using option 1 is that students get to work with large numbers as they attempt to spend as close as possible to the salary cap. Moreover, in addition to circle graphs, students will construct stacked-bar and multi-line graphs to track player performance over time because they will use the same players for the duration of the game.

Finally, in option 1, if a player is determined to be out for the year, students can use the portion of the salary cap they spent on that player to purchase another player.

For all of these reasons, option 1 is recommended.

Option 2: Different Teams Each Week

Each week, students select one team. For example, a student who lives in Atlanta may decide to select her hometown team for the first week of the game. However, she will not be allowed to choose that team in later weeks because each student can select the same team only once during the game. Two or more students can select the same team in a given week. Unlike in option 1, points are earned in this option from team statistics rather than from the statistics of individual players. For example, if a team had a total of 127 yards rushing, that is the number the student would use to compute points.

In this option, it is important for students to select high-scoring teams playing against weak opponents in order to maximize the points they earn. That said, there is as much luck involved in Fantasy Football as there is skill.

If you use option 1 to select players, students' rosters will remain the same for the duration of the game (with the exception of trades, which are explained later in the chapter). If you use option 2, students' players will change every week. *Note that the handouts, graphs, and worksheets in this book are based on option 1.*

Choosing Your Own Team

Like your students, you too should create your own fantasy team. You can use your team as an example and to help assess students' work. Students also enjoy competing with their teachers or parents!

Trades

Students may trade players if they are using option 1. In this situation, salary cap numbers do not apply. When a trade is consummated, the students making that trade must alter their fantasy team roster.

Trades do not have to be position for position. For example, a student might trade a kicker for a quarterback. But in that case, the student would have only one kicker. If that player was injured, the student would be left in a difficult position, without a kicker in his or her starting lineup. Students therefore need to be aware of the impact of trades on their full rosters.

Based on my experience with this game, you may want to limit the number of trades to five or ten per student. Otherwise, some students may make so many trades they cannot remember who is on their team.

Injuries and Bye Weeks

If you cannot locate a player's name in the box scores, he is probably injured or the teams didn't play that week (this is called a *bye week*). *If this occurs, the players' score is counted as zero.* A player who is placed on injured reserve (IR) will not play for the remainder of the season. If a player is declared out for the year and students are using option 1, a student who had selected that player can use the portion of the salary cap spent on that player to purchase another player. A list of injured players can be found in newspapers as well as online at fantasysportsmath.com or other sports Web sites.

Step 2: Reading Box Scores

Box scores are written in several formats. The sections of box scores you will use are usually titled "Scoring Summary" and "Player (or Individual) Statistics." A player (other than a kicker) whose name is listed in the scoring summary has scored a touchdown or passed for a touchdown. (The only exception is a two-point conversion, which occurs when a team elects to try for two points rather than kick the point after a touchdown. On a two-point conversion, a team gets one chance to get the ball in the end zone from the two-yard line.)

Table 1.2 shows one section of a fabricated box score. You will see that the first score of the game was a three-yard touchdown run by Aaron Dunlap. Additional touchdowns were scored in the second quarter by Frank Loery, Devan Shalter, Gary Hollings, and Ollie Mays. In addition, Steve Blake and Jesse Wade passed for touchdowns in the second quarter.

Kickers earn points for field goals (FG) and the point after touchdown (PAT). Notice, for example, that Angel Ramos kicked the point after touchdown after the first touchdown of the game. He also kicked a field goal in the first quarter.

The touchdowns scored by Devan Shalter and Gary Hollings were scored by players on defensive teams. Therefore, students who had the Panthers or Tigers as their defensive team would earn points. Defensive touchdowns are preceded by phrases such as "interception return," "fumble return," "punt return," "kick-off return," or "fumble recovery in end zone." Defensive teams also earn points for safeties, which occur when an offensive player is tackled in his own end zone. Safeties are listed as such and are rare; there were not any safeties in this game.

Table 1.2. Sample Box Score: Panthers at Tigers

1ST QUARTER	
TD	Aaron Dunlap, 3 Yd run (Angel Ramos kick is good), 9:59. Drive: 9 plays, 63 yards in 5:01.
FG	Angel Ramos 38 Yd, 2:00. Drive: 8 plays, 76 yards in 4:31.
2ND QUARTER	
TD	Frank Loery, 8 Yd pass from Steve Blake (Angel Ramos kick is good), 13:43. Drive: 6 plays, 27 yards in 3:08.
TD	Devan Shalter, 40 Yd interception return (Henry Darris 2 Pt. Conversion pass to failed), 4:41.
TD	Gary Hollings, 96 Yd kick return (Angel Ramos kick is good), 4:27.
TD	Ollie Mays, 7 Yd pass from Jesse Wade (Brian Martinez kick is good), 1:14. Drive: 5 plays, 50 yards in 1:26.
3RD QUARTER	
FG	Brian Martinez 44 Yd, 12:14. Drive: 8 plays, 26 yards in 2:46.
TD	Mack Knightly, 3 Yd pass from Jesse Wade (Jesse Wade pass to Ty Johnson for 2 Pt. Conversion), 1:54. Drive: 4 plays, 60 yards in 1:41.
4TH QUARTER	
FG	Brian Martinez 37 Yd, 11:38. Drive: 9 plays, 71 yards in 3:49.
TD	D. J. Tucker, 1 Yd pass from Jesse Wade (Brian Martinez kick is good), 8:57. Drive: 6 plays, 25 yards in 2:33.
FG	Brian Martinez 26 Yd, 3:22. Drive: 9 plays, 33 yards in 3:48.
TD	Gary Hollings, 15 Yd pass from Steve Blake (Angel Ramos kick is good), 1:24. Drive: 8 plays, 75 yards in 1:58.

Note: TD = touchdown. FG = field goal.

Players lose points for interceptions thrown and fumbles lost. The box score in Table 1.3 shows that Jesse Wade threw one interception (INT), and Gary Hollings and Josh Maris each lost one fumble.

The starting lineup in Table 1.4 is used for reference purposes throughout this book.

Step 3: Collecting Data

Each week, students use newspapers or online resources to access data from one game in which each of the players in their starting lineup participated. There are several options for collecting data:

1. Enroll your class in a newspapers-in-education program in order to receive free copies of newspapers.
2. If it is not possible to enroll in a newspapers-in-education program, choose a couple of students to cut box scores out of a newspaper and make copies for the other students. Students can reference the football standings in the newspaper to ensure that they have cut out a box score for each team that played that week.

3. Have students go to www.fantasysportsmath.com and do the following:
   a. Click the "Get Football Stats" link.
   b. On the following page, use the calendar to select the week you are looking for.
   c. Find a team one of your players participated in and click on the box score for that game.

Using online resources is the quickest and easiest method. Statistics are also archived online so that students can access data in case they missed a week or two.

Table 1.3. Box Score: Panthers at Tigers (Week 1)

PASSING—Panthers				
	CP/AT	YDS	TD	INT
J. Wade	33/48	369	3	1
PASSING—Tigers				
	CP/AT	YDS	TD	INT
S. Blake	19/30	221	2	2
RUSHING—Panthers				
	ATT	YDS	TD	LG
T. Johnson	9	15	0	7
L. Jones	4	14	0	8
J. Wade	4	−1	0	2
RUSHING—Tigers				
	ATT	YDS	TD	LG
A. Dunlap	18	84	1	16
J. Maris	7	34	0	21
Y. Ussif	1	23	0	23
S. Blake	1	3	0	3
RECEIVING—Panthers				
	REC	YDS	TD	LG
O. Mays	11	171	1	30
D. J. Tucker	9	67	1	19
T. Johnson	6	33	0	11
M. Knightly	7	98	1	31

(Cont'd.)

Table 1.3. Box Score: Panthers at Tigers (Week 1) *(Cont'd.)*

RECEIVING—Tigers				
	REC	YDS	TD	LG
F. Loery	7	109	1	49
G. Hollings	4	45	1	22
M. Sallinger	1	38	0	38
Y. Ussif	5	24	0	10
T. Faumuina	2	5	0	4
FUMBLES—Panthers				
	FUM	LOST	REC	YDS
C. Vickman	1	1	0	0
FUMBLES—Tigers				
	FUM	LOST	REC	YDS
G. Hollings	1	1	0	0
J. Maris	1	1	0	0
KICKING—Panthers				
	FG	LG	XP	PTS
B. Martinez	3/4	44	2/2	11
KICKING—Tigers				
	FG	LG	XP	PTS
A. Ramos	1/1	38	4/4	7

Note: cp = number of completed passes; at = number of passes attempted; yds = number of yards gained; td = number of touchdowns; int = number of interceptions; att = number of rushing attempts; lg = longest(gain); rec = number of receptions; fum = number of fumbles; lost = number of fumbles lost; rec = number of fumbles recovered; fg = field goal; lg = longest(field goal); xp = number of extra points(or PATs); pts = number of points scored

Table 1.4. Starting Lineup for the Wildcats

Jesse Wade	Quarterback
Ty Johnson	Running back
Josh Maris	Running back
Ollie Mays	Wide receiver
D. J. Tucker	Wide receiver
Tao Faumuina	Wide receiver
Angel Ramos	Kicker
Tigers	Defense

Step 4: Computing Points

The default scoring system (see Table 1.5) can be used each week to determine the ranking of students' teams in the game. The default scoring system was designed so that students can plot the weekly points earned for their players to precise numerical values on stacked-bar and multiple-line graphs. This is explained later. However, if you wish, you may choose a different scoring system to meet your students' skill level. The default scoring system is one of 111 included in this book. Scoring systems are dynamic because they give students opportunities to work with roots, exponents, summations, factorials, integers, fractions, decimals, and absolute value.

The default scoring system is dynamic because it uses all factors of 48—for example, two touchdowns equal one-fourth, and one touchdown and one two-point conversion equal one-sixth.

Table 1.5. Default Scoring System

For Each:	Players Earn:		
Kickers			
Point after touchdown (PAT)	$\frac{1}{48}$	or	.021
Field goal (FG)	$\frac{1}{16}$	or	.063
Quarterbacks, running backs, wide receivers, defenses			
Touchdown (by passing, rushing, or receiving)	$\frac{1}{8}$	or	.125
Two point conversion	$\frac{1}{24}$	or	.042
Touchdown by a defense	$\frac{1}{8}$	or	.125
Safety by a defense	$\frac{1}{24}$	or	.042
Interception	$-\frac{1}{12}$	or	−.083
Fumble	$-\frac{1}{16}$	or	−.063
Passing yards	$\frac{1}{48}$ for every 25 yards		
Rushing or receiving yards	$\frac{1}{48}$ for every 10 yards		

Note: Decimals are rounded to the nearest thousandth.

The points that players earn can be computed using two different methods. One method uses algebra, and the other does not. If students use both methods to compute points, they can verify their results. If they do not have the skills to work with variables in linear equations, they can use the non-algebraic method to compute points.

Non-Algebraic Method

The non-algebraic method lists touchdowns, two-point conversions, and yards gained for each player. Points are earned for each set of 25 yards gained from passing, as well as each set of 10 yards gained from rushing or receiving. Consequently, yards gained from passing are divided by 25, and yards gained from rushing or receiving are divided by 10. Quotients are always rounded down to the nearest whole number. For example, Jesse Wade passed for 369 yards, which is divided by 25. The quotient of 14.76 is rounded down to 14. Since there are 14 25s in 369 and each 25 yards is worth $\frac{1}{48}$, 14 is multiplied by $\frac{1}{48}$ to arrive at $\frac{14}{48}$. This process is also used to compute points earned from rushing and receiving yards, with the exception that students compute the number of 10s rather than the number of 25s.

Table 1.6 uses the non-algebraic method to compute the points for the Wildcats. I recommend using this method for the first few weeks before introducing students to the second method.

Algebraic Method

The second method of computing points is algebraic; it uses linear equations that contain variables. These equations are known as *total points equations* because they are used to compute the total points for one week for all players, with the exception of kickers and team defenses. Younger students may be initially intimidated by the algebraic look of the equations. However, once they have used them a few times, they become comfortable and feel proud that they are doing algebra.

Default Total Points Equation for Quarterbacks, Running Backs, and Wide Receivers

The default total points equation (the algebraic method) and the default scoring system (the non-algebraic method) contain the same numerical values. Consequently, students can check their work if they use both methods because both methods will result in the same answer.

$$\frac{1}{8}(T) + \frac{1}{24}(V) + \frac{1}{48}(P + R + C) - \frac{1}{12}(I) - \frac{1}{16}(F) = W$$

T = number of touchdowns scored by passing, rushing, or receiving
V = number of two-point conversions scored by passing, rushing, or receiving
P = number of passing yards divided by 25, then rounded down to the nearest whole number

Table 1.6. Points Earned by the Wildcats: Non-Algebraic Method

	Wade	Johnson	Maris	Mays	Tucker	Faumuina	Ramos	Tigers
Number of TDs $\times \frac{1}{8}$	$\frac{3}{8}$	0	0	$\frac{1}{8}$	$\frac{1}{8}$	0	0	$\frac{1}{8}$
Number of 2-point conversions or safeties $\times \frac{1}{24}$	$\frac{1}{24}$	$\frac{1}{24}$	0	0	0	0	0	0
Number of passing yards (in 25s) $\times \frac{1}{48}$	$\frac{14}{48}$	0	0	0	0	0	0	0
Number of rushing yards (in 10s) $\times \frac{1}{48}$	0	$\frac{1}{48}$	$\frac{3}{48}$	0	0	0	0	0
Number of receiving yards (in 10s) $\times \frac{1}{48}$	0	$\frac{3}{48}$	0	$\frac{17}{48}$	$\frac{6}{48}$	0	0	0
Number of PATs $\times \frac{1}{48}$	0	0	0	0	0	0	$\frac{4}{48}$	0
Number of FGs $\times \frac{1}{16}$	0	0	0	0	0	0	$\frac{1}{16}$	0
Number of interceptions $\times \left(-\frac{1}{12}\right)$	$-\frac{1}{12}$	0	0	0	0	0	0	0
Number of fumbles lost $\times \left(-\frac{1}{16}\right)$	0	0	$-\frac{1}{16}$	0	0	0	0	0
Total individual points:	$\frac{30}{48}$	$\frac{6}{48}$	0	$\frac{23}{48}$	$\frac{12}{48}$	0	$\frac{7}{48}$	$\frac{1}{8}$
Total team points: $\frac{30}{48} + \frac{6}{48} + \frac{23}{48} + \frac{12}{48} + \frac{7}{48} + \frac{1}{8} = \frac{84}{48} = 1\frac{36}{48} = 1\frac{3}{4}$								

R = number of rushing yards divided by 10, then rounded down to the nearest whole number

C = number of receiving yards divided by 10, then rounded down to the nearest whole number

I = number of interceptions thrown

F = number of fumbles lost

W = total points scored for one week for one individual player

Example Using Default Total Points Equation:

Points Earned for the Wildcats

Jesse Wade

$$\frac{1}{8}(3) + \frac{1}{24}(1) + \frac{1}{48}(14 + 0 + 0) - \frac{1}{12}(1) - \frac{1}{16}(0) = \frac{5}{8}$$

Ty Johnson

$$\frac{1}{8}(0) + \frac{1}{24}(1) + \frac{1}{48}(0 + 1 + 3) - \frac{1}{12}(0) - \frac{1}{16}(0) = \frac{1}{8}$$

Josh Maris

$$\frac{1}{8}(0) + \frac{1}{24}(0) + \frac{1}{48}(0 + 3 + 0) - \frac{1}{12}(0) - \frac{1}{16}(1) = 0$$

Ollie Mays

$$\frac{1}{8}(1) + \frac{1}{24}(0) + \frac{1}{48}(0 + 0 + 17) - \frac{1}{12}(0) - \frac{1}{16}(0) = \frac{23}{48}$$

D. J. Tucker

$$\frac{1}{8}(1) + \frac{1}{24}(0) + \frac{1}{48}(0 + 0 + 6) - \frac{1}{12}(0) - \frac{1}{16}(0) = \frac{1}{4}$$

Tao Faumuina

$$\frac{1}{8}(0) + \frac{1}{24}(0) + \frac{1}{48}(0 + 0 + 0) - \frac{1}{12}(0) - \frac{1}{16}(0) = 0$$

Angel Ramos

$$4 \text{ PATs}\left(4 \cdot \frac{1}{48}\right) + 1 \text{ FG}\left(\frac{1}{16}\right) = \frac{7}{48}$$

Tigers Defense

$$1 \text{ touchdown} = \frac{1}{8}$$

Total points for the Wildcats $\frac{84}{48} = 1\frac{36}{48} = 1\frac{3}{4}$ or 1.75

Additional Scoring Systems

The following pages list 111 scoring systems. Choose a system that is appropriate for the skill level of your students. If students are not prepared to use variables in linear equations, you can still use any scoring system by simply using the values from any total points equation. Let's say that for a few weeks, you use the default scoring system, which is based on a common denominator of 48. If you want students to practice with a different common denominator (or practice with decimals, exponents, roots, or something else), you could use numerical values from a different equation. Students should use the same scoring system throughout the game in order to determine their cumulative points so they can update their stacked-bar and multiple-line graphs. Introduce new scoring systems when your students are ready.

Scoring systems are categorized according to their content and whether they contain relative proportionality. For example, scoring systems number six and ten (located below) use relative proportionality because the ratios between the fractions in each equation are the same. In other words, a touchdown is worth twice as much as a field goal, three times as much as a safety, and six times as much as an extra point.

6. $\frac{1}{2}(T) + \frac{1}{6}(V) + \frac{1}{12}(P + R + C) - \frac{1}{3}(I) - \frac{1}{4}(F) = W$

$\text{FG} = \frac{1}{4} \qquad \text{PAT} = \frac{1}{12} \qquad \text{Safety} = \frac{1}{6}$

10. $\frac{1}{4}(T) + \frac{1}{12}(V) + \frac{1}{24}(P + R + C) - \frac{1}{6}(I) - \frac{1}{8}(F) = W$

$\text{FG} = \frac{1}{8} \qquad \text{PAT} = \frac{1}{24} \qquad \text{Safety} = \frac{1}{12}$

The advantage of scoring systems that use relative proportionality is that you can use these different scoring systems during the course of the game without unfairly changing the rankings. In other words, a student whose team earned the highest number of points in a given week will earn the highest number of points in that week no matter which scoring systems are used, as long as the scoring systems are proportionate. Conversely, let's say you used a scoring system that was based on fractions for the first ten weeks, then used a different scoring system for week 11 that was based on factorials and not proportionate to the original scoring system you used. It is possible that the student who was in last place after ten weeks could leap into first place after week 11 if her team performed strongly, because the scoring systems based on factorials are not proportionate and can result in teams earning hundreds of points in one week. Consequently, it's not fair for a student who has built up a small lead over the course of ten weeks to suddenly be hundreds of points out of the lead based on the results of one week. For this reason, I suggest using the same scoring system or scoring systems that are proportionate throughout the game in order to determine standings. If you wish to include other scoring systems, I would not include these to determine the rankings of the students' teams. Scoring systems 4 to 25 and 29 to 70 contain relative proportionality.

Many scoring systems (that is, total points equations) are more advanced than the default scoring system, especially those that are based on negative numerical values. In such cases, the goal is to acquire the fewest points (or the greatest absolute value). Acquiring the fewest points is an effective way to teach the concept of absolute value. In the following example, a player might earn $\frac{7}{48}$ if a student used scoring system number four. However, if the student placed absolute value symbols around scoring system number five before using it to compute points, the player would also earn $\frac{7}{48}$.

$$4.\ \frac{1}{8}(2) + \frac{1}{24}(0) + \frac{1}{48}(9 + 1 + 0) - \frac{1}{12}(3) - \frac{1}{16}(1) = \frac{7}{48}$$

$$5.\ \left| -\frac{1}{8}(2) - \frac{1}{24}(0) - \frac{1}{48}(9 + 1 + 0) + \frac{1}{12}(3) + \frac{1}{16}(1) \right| = \frac{7}{48}$$

Consequently, students can check their work by computing points earned using both positive and negative versions of the same scoring system since both answers will result in the same absolute value. In order to do this, you may simply insert absolute value symbols around any equation that is based on negative numerical values.

It is possible (although unlikely) for a player to earn a negative number of points even if students are using equations based on positive numerical values. In other words, a player may have a bad game statistically and not generate enough positive points to offset the negative points earned by his interceptions or fumbles. You can prevent this situation by using equation 2 below or by informing students that the lowest score for one week will be zero, thus ensuring that younger students will not be confused by negative numerical values.

Total Points Equations

Integers

1. $6(T) + 2(V) + 3(P + R + C) - 1(I) - 1(F) = W$

   FG = 3 PAT = 1 Safety = 2

2. $6(T) + 2(V) + 1(P + R + C) = W$

   FG = 3 PAT = 1 Safety = 2

3. $-6(T) - 2(V) - 1(P + R + C) + 4(I) + 3(F) = W$

   FG = 3 PAT = 1 Safety = 2

Fractions

4. $\frac{1}{8}(T) + \frac{1}{24}(V) + \frac{1}{48}(P + R + C) - \frac{1}{12}(I) - \frac{1}{16}(F) = W$

   FG $= \frac{1}{16}$ PAT $= \frac{1}{48}$ Safety $= \frac{1}{24}$

5. $-\frac{1}{8}(T) - \frac{1}{24}(V) - \frac{1}{48}(P + R + C) + \frac{1}{12}(I) + \frac{1}{16}(F) = W$

   FG $= -\frac{1}{16}$ PAT $= -\frac{1}{48}$ Safety $= -\frac{1}{24}$

6. $\frac{1}{2}(T) + \frac{1}{6}(V) + \frac{1}{12}(P + R + C) - \frac{1}{3}(I) - \frac{1}{4}(F) = W$

   FG $= \frac{1}{4}$ PAT $= \frac{1}{12}$ Safety $= \frac{1}{6}$

7. $-\frac{1}{2}(T) - \frac{1}{6}(V) - \frac{1}{12}(P + R + C) + \frac{1}{3}(I) + \frac{1}{4}(F) = W$

FG $= -\frac{1}{4}$ PAT $= -\frac{1}{12}$ Safety $= -\frac{1}{6}$

8. $\frac{1}{3}(T) + \frac{1}{9}(V) + \frac{1}{18}(P + R + C) - \frac{1}{4.5}(I) - \frac{1}{6}(F) = W$

FG $= \frac{1}{6}$ PAT $= \frac{1}{18}$ Safety $= \frac{1}{9}$

9. $-\frac{1}{3}(T) - \frac{1}{9}(V) - \frac{1}{18}(P + R + C) + \frac{1}{4.5}(I) + \frac{1}{6}(F) = W$

FG $= -\frac{1}{6}$ PAT $= -\frac{1}{18}$ Safety $= -\frac{1}{9}$

10. $\frac{1}{4}(T) + \frac{1}{12}(V) + \frac{1}{24}(P + R + C) - \frac{1}{6}(I) - \frac{1}{8}(F) = W$

FG $= \frac{1}{8}$ PAT $= \frac{1}{24}$ Safety $= \frac{1}{12}$

11. $-\frac{1}{4}(T) - \frac{1}{12}(V) - \frac{1}{24}(P + R + C) + \frac{1}{6}(I) + \frac{1}{8}(F) = W$

FG $= -\frac{1}{8}$ PAT $= -\frac{1}{24}$ Safety $= -\frac{1}{12}$

12. $\frac{1}{5}(T) + \frac{1}{15}(V) + \frac{1}{30}(P + R + C) - \frac{1}{7.5}(I) - \frac{1}{10}(F) = W$

FG $= \frac{1}{10}$ PAT $= \frac{1}{30}$ Safety $= \frac{1}{15}$

13. $-\frac{1}{5}(T) - \frac{1}{15}(V) - \frac{1}{30}(P + R + C) + \frac{1}{7.5}(I) + \frac{1}{10}(F) = W$

FG $= -\frac{1}{10}$ PAT $= -\frac{1}{30}$ Safety $= -\frac{1}{15}$

14. $\frac{1}{6}(T) + \frac{1}{18}(V) + \frac{1}{36}(P + R + C) - \frac{1}{9}(I) - \frac{1}{12}(F) = W$

FG $= \frac{1}{12}$ PAT $= \frac{1}{36}$ Safety $= \frac{1}{18}$

15. $-\frac{1}{6}(T) - \frac{1}{18}(V) - \frac{1}{36}(P + R + C) + \frac{1}{9}(I) + \frac{1}{12}(F) = W$

FG $= -\frac{1}{12}$ PAT $= -\frac{1}{36}$ Safety $= -\frac{1}{18}$

16. $\frac{1}{7}(T) + \frac{1}{21}(V) + \frac{1}{42}(P + R + C) - \frac{1}{10.5}(I) - \frac{1}{14}(F) = W$

FG $= \frac{1}{14}$ PAT $= \frac{1}{42}$ Safety $= \frac{1}{21}$

17. $-\frac{1}{7}(T) - \frac{1}{21}(V) - \frac{1}{42}(P + R + C) + \frac{1}{10.5}(I) + \frac{1}{14}(F) = W$

FG $= -\frac{1}{14}$ PAT $= -\frac{1}{42}$ Safety $= -\frac{1}{21}$

18. $\frac{1}{9}(T) + \frac{1}{27}(V) + \frac{1}{54}(P + R + C) - \frac{1}{13.5}(I) - \frac{1}{18}(F) = W$

FG $= \frac{1}{18}$ PAT $= \frac{1}{54}$ Safety $= \frac{1}{27}$

19. $-\frac{1}{9}(T) - \frac{1}{27}(V) - \frac{1}{54}(P + R + C) + \frac{1}{13.5}(I) + \frac{1}{18}(F) = W$

FG $= -\frac{1}{18}$ PAT $= -\frac{1}{54}$ Safety $= -\frac{1}{27}$

20. $\frac{1}{10}(T) + \frac{1}{30}(V) + \frac{1}{60}(P + R + C) - \frac{1}{15}(I) - \frac{1}{20}(F) = W$

FG $= \frac{1}{20}$ PAT $= \frac{1}{60}$ Safety $= \frac{1}{30}$

21. $-\frac{1}{10}(T) - \frac{1}{30}(V) - \frac{1}{60}(P + R + C) + \frac{1}{15}(I) + \frac{1}{20}(F) = W$

FG $= -\frac{1}{20}$ PAT $= -\frac{1}{60}$ Safety $= -\frac{1}{30}$

22. $\frac{1}{25}(T) + \frac{1}{75}(V) + \frac{1}{150}(P + R + C) - \frac{1}{37.5}(I) - \frac{1}{50}(F) = W$

FG $= \frac{1}{50}$ PAT $= \frac{1}{150}$ Safety $= \frac{1}{75}$

23. $-\frac{1}{25}(T) - \frac{1}{75}(V) - \frac{1}{150}(P + R + C) + \frac{1}{37.5}(I) + \frac{1}{50}(F) = W$

FG $= -\frac{1}{50}$ PAT $= -\frac{1}{150}$ Safety $= -\frac{1}{75}$

24. $\frac{1}{100}(T) + \frac{1}{300}(V) + \frac{1}{600}(P + R + C) - \frac{1}{150}(I) - \frac{1}{200}(F) = W$

FG $= \frac{1}{200}$ PAT $= \frac{1}{600}$ Safety $= \frac{1}{300}$

25. $-\frac{1}{100}(T) - \frac{1}{300}(V) - \frac{1}{600}(P + R + C) + \frac{1}{150}(I) + \frac{1}{200}(F) = W$

FG $= -\frac{1}{200}$ PAT $= -\frac{1}{600}$ Safety $= -\frac{1}{300}$

26. $\frac{5}{6}(T) + \frac{4}{5}(V) + \frac{3}{4}(P + R + C) - \frac{2}{7}(I) - \frac{2}{8}(F) = W$

FG $= \frac{2}{8}$ PAT $= \frac{3}{4}$ Safety $= \frac{4}{5}$

27. $\frac{1}{2}(T) + \frac{1}{3}(V) + \frac{1}{4}(P + R + C) - \frac{1}{5}(I) - \frac{1}{6}(F) = W$

FG $= \frac{1}{6}$ PAT $= \frac{1}{4}$ Safety $= \frac{1}{3}$

28. $\frac{1}{2}(T) + \frac{1}{4}(V) + \frac{1}{8}(P + R + C) - \frac{1}{16}(I) - \frac{1}{32}(F) = W$

FG $= \frac{1}{32}$ PAT $= \frac{1}{8}$ Safety $= \frac{1}{4}$

Decimals

29. $.006\,(T) + .002\,(V) + .001\,(P + R + C) - .004\,(I) - .003\,(F) = W$
    FG = .003 PAT = .001 Safety = .002
30. $-.006\,(T) - .002\,(V) - .001\,(P + R + C) + .004\,(I) + .003\,(F) = W$
    FG = −.003 PAT = −.001 Safety = −.002
31. $.075\,(T) + .025\,(V) + .0125\,(P + R + C) - .05\,(I) - .0375\,(F) = W$
    FG = .0375 PAT = .0125 Safety = .025
32. $-.075\,(T) - .025\,(V) - .0125\,(P + R + C) + .05\,(I) + .0375\,(F) = W$
    FG = −.0375 PAT = −.0125 Safety = −.025
33. $.06\,(T) + .02\,(V) + .01\,(P + R + C) - .04\,(I) - .03\,(F) = W$
    FG = .03 PAT = .01 Safety = .02
34. $-.06\,(T) - .02\,(V) - .01\,(P + R + C) + .04\,(I) + .03\,(F) = W$
    FG = −.03 PAT = −.01 Safety = −.02
35. $.1\,(T) + .0\overline{3}\,(V) + .01\overline{6}\,(P + R + C) - .0\overline{6}\,(I) - .05\,(F) = W$
    FG = .05 PAT = $.01\overline{6}$ Safety = $.0\overline{3}$
36. $-.1\,(T) - .0\overline{3}\,(V) - .01\overline{6}\,(P + R + C) + .0\overline{6}\,(I) + .05\,(F) = W$
    FG = −.05 PAT = $-.01\overline{6}$ Safety = $-.0\overline{3}$
37. $.1\,(T) + .05\,(V) + .025\,(P + R + C) - .1\,(I) - .075\,(F) = W$
    FG = .075 PAT = .025 Safety = .05
38. $-.15\,(T) - .05\,(V) - .025\,(P + R + C) + .1\,(I) + .075\,(F) = W$
    FG = −.075 PAT = −.025 Safety = −.05
39. $.3\,(T) + .1\,(V) + .05\,(P + R + C) - .2\,(I) - .15\,(F) = W$
    FG = .15 PAT = .05 Safety = .1
40. $-.3\,(T) - .1\,(V) - .05\,(P + R + C) + .2\,(I) + .15\,(F) = W$
    FG = −.15 PAT = −.05 Safety = −.1
41. $.6\,(T) + .2\,(V) + .1\,(P + R + C) - .4\,(I) - .3\,(F) = W$
    FG = .3 PAT = .1 Safety = .2
42. $-.6\,(T) - .2\,(V) - .1\,(P + R + C) + .4\,(I) + .3\,(F) = W$
    FG = −.3 PAT = −.1 Safety = −.2
43. $.9\,(T) + .3\,(V) + .15\,(P + R + C) - .6\,(I) - .45\,(F) = W$
    FG = .45 PAT = .15 Safety = .3
44. $-.9\,(T) - .3\,(V) - .15\,(P + R + C) + .6\,(I) + .45\,(F) = W$
    FG = −.45 PAT = −.15 Safety = −.3

Fractions and Decimals

45. $.25\,(T) + \frac{1}{12}\,(V) + \frac{1}{24}\,(P + R + C) - \frac{1}{6}\,(I) - .125\,(F) = W$
    FG = .125 PAT = $\frac{1}{24}$ Safety = $\frac{1}{12}$

46. $-.25\,(T) - \frac{1}{12}\,(V) - \frac{1}{24}\,(P + R + C) + \frac{1}{6}\,(I) + .125\,(F) = W$

FG $= -.125$ PAT $= -\frac{1}{24}$ Safety $= -\frac{1}{12}$

47. $.2\,(T) + \frac{1}{15}\,(V) + \frac{1}{30}\,(P + R + C) - \frac{1}{7.5}\,(I) - .1\,(F) = W$

FG $= .1$ PAT $= \frac{1}{30}$ Safety $= \frac{1}{15}$

48. $-.2\,(T) - \frac{1}{15}\,(V) - \frac{1}{30}\,(P + R + C) + \frac{1}{7.5}\,(I) + .1\,(F) = W$

FG $= -.1$ PAT $= -\frac{1}{30}$ Safety $= -\frac{1}{15}$

49. $.1\,(T) + \frac{1}{30}\,(V) + \frac{1}{60}\,(P + R + C) - \frac{1}{15}\,(I) - .5\,(F) = W$

FG $= .5$ PAT $= \frac{1}{60}$ Safety $= \frac{1}{30}$

50. $-.1\,(T) - \frac{1}{30}\,(V) - \frac{1}{60}\,(P + R + C) + \frac{1}{15}\,(I) + .5\,(F) = W$

FG $= -.5$ PAT $= -\frac{1}{60}$ Safety $= -\frac{1}{30}$

51. $.04\,(T) + \frac{1}{75}\,(V) + \frac{1}{150}\,(P + R + C) - \frac{1}{37.5}\,(I) - .02\,(F) = W$

FG $= .02$ PAT $= \frac{1}{150}$ Safety $= \frac{1}{75}$

52. $-.04\,(T) - \frac{1}{75}\,(V) - \frac{1}{150}\,(P + R + C) + \frac{1}{37.5}\,(I) + .02\,(F) = W$

FG $= -.02$ PAT $= -\frac{1}{150}$ Safety $= -\frac{1}{75}$

53. $.01(T) + \frac{1}{300}\,(V) + \frac{1}{600}\,(P + R + C) - \frac{1}{150}\,(I) - .005\,(F) = W$

FG $= .005$ PAT $= \frac{1}{600}$ Safety $= \frac{1}{300}$

54. $-.01\,(T) - \frac{1}{300}\,(V) - \frac{1}{600}\,(P + R + C) + \frac{1}{150}\,(I) + .005\,(F) = W$

FG $= -.005$ PAT $= -\frac{1}{600}$ Safety $= -\frac{1}{300}$

55. $\frac{3}{500}\,(T) + .002\,(V) + \frac{1}{1000}\,(P + R + C) - .004\,(I) - \frac{3}{1000}\,(F) = W$

FG $= \frac{3}{1000}$ PAT $= .001$ Safety $= \frac{1}{500}$

56. $-\frac{3}{500}(T) - .002\ (V) - \frac{1}{1000}(P + R + C) + .004\ (I) + \frac{3}{1000}(F) = W$

FG $= -\frac{3}{1000}$ PAT $= -.001$ Safety $= -\frac{1}{500}$

57. $\frac{3}{40}(T) + .025\ (V) + .0125\ (P + R + C) - \frac{1}{20}(I) - .0375\ (F) = W$

FG $= .0375$ PAT $= \frac{1}{80}$ Safety $= .025$

58. $-\frac{3}{40}(T) - .025\ (V) - .0125\ (P + R + C) + \frac{1}{20}(I) + .0375\ (F) = W$

FG $= -.0375$ PAT $= -\frac{1}{80}$ Safety $= -.025$

59. $.06\ (T) + \frac{1}{50}(V) + .01(P + R + C) - \frac{1}{25}(I) - .03\ (F) = W$

FG $= .03$ PAT $= \frac{1}{100}$ Safety $= .02$

60. $-.06\ (T) - \frac{1}{50}(V) - .01\ (P + R + C) + \frac{1}{25}(I) + .03\ (F) = W$

FG $= -.03$ PAT $= -\frac{1}{100}$ Safety $= -.02$

61. $\frac{1}{10}(T) + .0\overline{3}\ (V) + .01\overline{6}\ (P + R + C) - .0\overline{6}\ (I) - \frac{1}{20}(F) = W$

FG $= \frac{1}{20}$ PAT $= .01\overline{6}$ Safety $= .0\overline{3}$

62. $-\frac{1}{10}(T) - .0\overline{3}\ (V) - .01\overline{6}\ (P + R + C) + .0\overline{6}\ (I) + \frac{1}{20}(F) = W$

FG $= -\frac{1}{20}$ PAT $= -.01\overline{6}$ Safety $= -.0\overline{3}$

63. $.15\ (T) + \frac{1}{20}(V) + .025\ (P + R + C) - \frac{1}{10}(I) - .075\ (F) = W$

FG $= .075$ PAT $= \frac{1}{40}$ Safety $= .05$

64. $-.15\ (T) - \frac{1}{20}(V) - .025\ (P + R + C) + \frac{1}{10}(I) + .075\ (F) = W$

FG $= -.075$ PAT $= -\frac{1}{40}$ Safety $= -.05$

65. $\frac{3}{10}(T) + .1\ (V) + \frac{1}{20}(P + R + C) - .2\ (I) - \frac{3}{20}(F) = W$

FG $= \frac{3}{20}$ PAT $= .05$ Safety $= \frac{1}{10}$

66. $-\frac{3}{10}(T) - .1(V) - \frac{1}{20}(P + R + C) + .2(I) + \frac{3}{20}(F) = W$

FG $= -\frac{3}{20}$ PAT $= -.05$ Safety $= -\frac{1}{10}$

67. $.6(T) + \frac{1}{5}(V) + .1(P + R + C) - \frac{2}{5}(I) - .3(F) = W$

FG $= .3$ PAT $= \frac{1}{10}$ Safety $= .2$

68. $-.6(T) - \frac{1}{5}(V) - .1(P + R + C) + \frac{2}{5}(I) + .3(F) = W$

FG $= -.3$ PAT $= -\frac{1}{10}$ Safety $= -.2$

69. $.9(T) + .3(V) + \frac{3}{20}(P + R + C) - \frac{3}{5}(I) - \frac{9}{20}(F) = W$

FG $= .45$ PAT $= \frac{3}{20}$ Safety $= .3$

70. $-.9(T) - .3(V) - \frac{3}{20}(P + R + C) + \frac{3}{5}(I) + \frac{9}{20}(F) = W$

FG $= -.45$ PAT $= -\frac{3}{20}$ Safety $= -.3$

Integers with Positive Exponents

71. $2^4(T) + 2^3(V) + 2^2(P + R + C) - 2^1(I) - 2^0(F) = W$
FG $= 2^2$ PAT $= 2^0$ Safety $= 2^3$

72. $-2^4(T) - 2^3(V) - 2^2(P + R + C) + 2^1(I) + 2^0(F) = W$
FG $= -2^2$ PAT $= -2^0$ Safety $= -2^3$

73. $3^4(T) + 3^3(V) + 3^2(P + R + C) - 3^1(I) - 3^0(F) = W$
FG $= 3^2$ PAT $= 3^0$ Safety $= 3^3$

74. $4^4(T) + 4^3(V) + 4^2(P + R + C) - 4^1(I) - 4^0(F) = W$
FG $= 4^2$ PAT $= 4^0$ Safety $= 4^3$

75. $-4^4(T) - 4^3(V) - 4^2(P + R + C) + 4^1(I) + 4^0(F) = W$
FG $= -4^2$ PAT $= -4^0$ Safety $= -4^3$

76. $5^4(T) + 5^3(V) + 5^2(P + R + C) - 5^1(I) - 5^0(F) = W$
FG $= 5^2$ PAT $= 5^0$ Safety $= 5^3$

77. $6^4(T) + 6^3(V) + 6^2(P + R + C) - 6^1(I) - 6^0(F) = W$
FG $= 6^2$ PAT $= 6^0$ Safety $= 6^3$

78. $-6^4(T) - 6^3(V) - 6^2(P + R + C) + 6^1(I) + 6^0(F) = W$
FG $= -6^2$ PAT $= -6^0$ Safety $= -6^3$

Integers with Negative Exponents

79. $2^0 (T) + 2^{-1} (V) + 2^{-2} (P + R + C) - 2^{-3} (I) - 2^{-4} (F) = W$
FG $= 2^{-4}$ PAT $= 2^{-2}$ Safety $= 2^{-1}$

80. $3^0 (T) + 3^{-1} (V) + 3^{-2}(P + R + C) - 3^{-3} (I) - 3^{-4}(F) = W$
FG $= 3^{-4}$ PAT $= 3^{-2}$ Safety $= 3^{-1}$

81. $-3^0 (T) - 3^{-1} (V) - 3^{-2} (P + R + C) + 3^{-3} (I) + 3^{-4} (F) = W$
FG $= -3^{-4}$ PAT $= -3^{-2}$ Safety $= -3^{-1}$

82. $4^0 (T) + 4^{-1} (V) + 4^{-2}(P + R + C) - 4^{-3}(I) - 4^{-4}(F) = W$
FG $= 4^{-4}$ PAT $= 4^{-2}$ Safety $= 4^{-1}$

83. $5^0 (T) + 5^{-1} (V) + 5^{-2} (P + R + C) - 5^{-3} (I) - 5^{-4} (F) = W$
FG $= 5^{-4}$ PAT $= 5^{-2}$ Safety $= 5^{-1}$

84. $-5^0 (T) - 5^{-1} (V) - 5^{-2} (P + R + C) + 5^{-3} (I) + 5^{-4} (F) = W$
FG $= -5^{-4}$ PAT $= -5^{-2}$ Safety $= -5^{-1}$

85. $6^0 (T) + 6^{-1} (V) + 6^{-2}(P + R + C) - 6^{-3} (I) - 6^{-4} (F) = W$
FG $= 6^{-4}$ PAT $= 6^{-2}$ Safety $= 6^{-1}$

Decimals with Positive Exponents

86. $.3^0 (T) + .3^1 (V) + .3^2 (P + R + C) - .3^3 (I) - .3^4 (F) = W$
FG $= .3^4$ PAT $= .3^2$ Safety $= .3^1$

87. $.4^0 (T) + .4^1 (V) + .4^2 (P + R + C) - .4^3 (I) - .4^4 (F) = W$
FG $= .4^4$ PAT $= .4^2$ Safety $= .4^1$

88. $.5^0 (T) + .5^1 (V) + .5^2 (P + R + C) - .5^3 (I) - .5^4 (F) = W$
FG $= .5^4$ PAT $= .5^2$ Safety $= .5^1$

89. $.6^0 (T) + .6^1 (V) + .6^2 (P + R + C) - .6^3 (I) - .6^4 (F) = W$
FG $= .6^4$ PAT $= .6^2$ Safety $= .6^1$

Decimals with Negative Exponents

90. $.3^{-4} (T) + .3^{-3} (V) + .3^{-2} (P + R + C) - .3^{-1} (I) - .3^0 (F) = W$
FG $= .3^0$ PAT $= .3^{-2}$ Safety $= .3^{-3}$

91. $.4^{-4} (T) + .4^{-3} (V) + .4^{-2} (P + R + C) - .4^{-1}(I) - .4^0 (F) = W$
FG $= .4^0$ PAT $= .4^{-2}$ Safety $= .4^{-3}$

92. $.5^{-4} (T) + .5^{-3} (V) + .5^{-2}(P + R + C) - .5^{-1}(I) - .5^0 (F) = W$
FG $= .5^0$ PAT $= .5^{-2}$ Safety $= .5^{-3}$

93. $.6^{-4} (T) + .6^{-3} (V) + .6^{-2}(P + R + C) - .6^{-1}(I) - .6^0 (F) = W$
FG $= .6^0$ PAT $= .6^{-2}$ Safety $= .6^{-3}$

Fractions with Positive Exponents

94. $\left(\frac{1}{2}\right)^0 (T) + \left(\frac{1}{2}\right)^1 (V) + \left(\frac{1}{2}\right)^2 (P + R + C) - \left(\frac{1}{2}\right)^3 (I) - \left(\frac{1}{2}\right)^4 (F) = W$

    FG $= \left(\frac{1}{2}\right)^4$ PAT $= \left(\frac{1}{2}\right)^2$ Safety $= \left(\frac{1}{2}\right)^1$

95. $\left(\frac{1}{3}\right)^0 (T) + \left(\frac{1}{3}\right)^1 (V) + \left(\frac{1}{3}\right)^2 (P + R + C) - \left(\frac{1}{3}\right)^3 (I) - \left(\frac{1}{3}\right)^4 (F) = W$

    FG $= \left(\frac{1}{3}\right)^4$ PAT $= \left(\frac{1}{3}\right)^2$ Safety $= \left(\frac{1}{3}\right)^1$

96. $\left(\frac{5}{6}\right)^0 (T) + \left(\frac{4}{5}\right)^1 (V) + \left(\frac{3}{4}\right)^2 (P + R + C) - \left(\frac{2}{7}\right)^3 (I) - \left(\frac{2}{8}\right)^4 (F) = W$

    FG $= \left(\frac{2}{8}\right)^4$ PAT $= \left(\frac{3}{4}\right)^2$ Safety $= \left(\frac{4}{5}\right)^1$

Fractions with Negative Exponents

97. $\left(\frac{2}{8}\right)^{-4} (T) + \left(\frac{2}{7}\right)^{-3} (V) + \left(\frac{3}{4}\right)^{-2} (P + R + C) - \left(\frac{4}{5}\right)^{-1} (I) - \left(\frac{5}{6}\right)^0 (F) = W$

    FG $= \left(\frac{5}{6}\right)^0$ PAT $= \left(\frac{3}{4}\right)^{-2}$ Safety $= \left(\frac{2}{7}\right)^{-3}$

98. $\left(\frac{1}{4}\right)^{-4} (T) + \left(\frac{1}{4}\right)^{-3} (V) + \left(\frac{1}{4}\right)^{-2} (P + R + C) - \left(\frac{1}{4}\right)^{-1} (I) - \left(\frac{1}{4}\right)^0 (F) = W$

    FG $= \left(\frac{1}{4}\right)^0$ PAT $= \left(\frac{1}{4}\right)^{-2}$ Safety $= \left(\frac{1}{4}\right)^{-3}$

Roots

99. $\sqrt{36}\,(T) + \sqrt{25}\,(V) + \sqrt{16}\,(P + R + C) - \sqrt{9}\,(I) - \sqrt{4}\,(F) = W$

    FG $= \sqrt{4}$ PAT $= \sqrt{16}$ Safety $= \sqrt{25}$

100. $-\sqrt{36}\,(T) - \sqrt{25}\,(V) - \sqrt{16}\,(P + R + C) + \sqrt{9}\,(I) + \sqrt{4}\,(F) = W$

    FG $= -\sqrt{4}$ PAT $= -\sqrt{16}$ Safety $= -\sqrt{25}$

101. $-\sqrt{121}\,(T) - \sqrt{100}\,(V) - \sqrt{81}\,(P + R + C) + \sqrt{64}\,(I) + \sqrt{49}\,(F) = W$

    FG $= \sqrt{49}$ PAT $= \sqrt{81}$ Safety $= \sqrt{100}$

102. $-\sqrt{121}\,(T) - \sqrt{100}\,(V) - \sqrt{81}\,(P + R + C) + \sqrt{64}\,(I) + \sqrt{49}\,(F)$

    FG $= -\sqrt{49}$ PAT $= -\sqrt{81}$ Safety $= -\sqrt{100}$

103. $\sqrt{25}\,(T) + \sqrt[3]{64}\,(V) + \sqrt[4]{81}\,(P + R + C) - \sqrt[5]{32}\,(I) - \sqrt[6]{1}\,(F) = W$

    FG $= \sqrt[6]{1}$ PAT $= \sqrt[4]{81}$ Safety $= \sqrt[3]{64}$

Factorials and Summations

104. $6!\,(T) + 5!\,(V) + 4!\,(P + R + C) - 3!\,(I) - 2!\,(F) = W$

FG = $4!$ PAT = $2!$ Safety = $5!$

105. $-6!\,(T) - 5!\,(V) - 4!\,(P + R + C) + 3!\,(I) + 2!\,(F) = W$

FG = $-4!$ PAT = $-2!$ Safety = $-5!$

106. $\left(\sum_{j=1}^{6} j\right)(T) + \left(\sum_{j=1}^{5} j\right)(V) + \left(\sum_{j=1}^{4} j\right)(P + R + C) - \left(\sum_{j=1}^{3} j\right)(I) - \left(\sum_{j=1}^{2} j\right)(F) = W$

FG = $\left(\sum_{j=1}^{4} j\right)$ PAT = $\left(\sum_{j=1}^{2} j\right) \sum 2$ Safety = $\left(\sum_{j=1}^{5} j\right)$

107. $-\left(\sum_{j=1}^{6} j\right)(T) - \left(\sum_{j=1}^{5} j\right)(V) - \left(\sum_{j=1}^{4} j\right)(P + R + C) + \left(\sum_{j=1}^{3} j\right)(I) + \left(\sum_{j=1}^{2} j\right)(F) = W$

FG = $-\left(\sum_{j=1}^{4} j\right)$ PAT = $\left(\sum_{j=1}^{2} j\right) - \sum 2$ Safety = $-\left(\sum_{j=1}^{5} j\right)$

Fractions, Decimals, Summations, Factorials, Exponents, Roots

108. $\left(\sum_{j=1}^{3} j\right)(T) + \left(\frac{2}{5}\right)^{-1}(V) + 2!\,(P + R + C) - \left(\frac{5}{6}\right)^{0}(I) - \left(\sqrt[4]{16}\right)^{-2}(F) = W$

FG = $\left(\sqrt[4]{16}\right)^{-2}$ PAT = $2!$ Safety = $\left(\frac{2}{5}\right)^{-1}$

109. $-\left(\sum_{j=1}^{3} j\right)(T) - \left(\frac{2}{5}\right)^{-1}(V) - 2!\,(P + R + C) + \left(\frac{5}{6}\right)^{0}(I) + \left(\sqrt[4]{16}\right)^{-2}(F) = W$

FG = $-\left(\sqrt[4]{16}\right)^{-2}$ PAT = $-2!$ Safety = $-\left(\frac{2}{5}\right)^{-1}$

110. $.2^{-3}\,(T) + 5!\,(V) + \left(\sum_{j=1}^{6} j\right)(P + R + C) - \sqrt[3]{64}\,(I) - .025\,(F) = W$

FG = $.025$ PAT = $\left(\sum_{j=1}^{6} j\right)$ Safety = $5!$

111. $-.2^{-3}(T) - 5!\,(V) - \left(\sum_{j=1}^{6} j\right)(P + R + C) + \sqrt[3]{64}\,(I) + .025\,(F) = W$

FG = $.025$ PAT = $\left(\sum_{j=1}^{6} j\right)$ Safety = $5!$

Chapter Two

Explaining Fantasy Football and Mathematics to Students: Handouts

This chapter contains the student handouts that you can reproduce for your students. Table 2.1 provides a description of each handout. The handouts are also included in the *Fantasy Football and Mathematics Student Workbook,* which accompanies this teacher's guide. Thus, if your students are using the student workbook, you do not need to make copies of these handouts.

Table 2.1. Descriptions of Handouts

Handout Number	Description
1	Description and rules of the game.
2	Fantasy team roster.
3	Example of a box score.
4	Step-by-step instructions on how to access statistics online.
5	The default scoring system. If you choose another scoring system, students will not receive this handout.
6	Practice in computing points for players on the Wildcats using the default scoring system.
7	Introduction of the default total points equation.
8	Practice in computing points for players on the Wildcats using the default total points equation.
9	Weekly scoring worksheet that uses the non-algebraic method to compute points. Students use one worksheet for each week. Fill in the number of the week on each worksheet.
10	Weekly scoring worksheet that uses the algebraic method (that is, total points equations). Students use one worksheet for each week. Fill in the number of the week on each worksheet.
11	Scoring sheet on which students can record their weekly points for posting on the bulletin board.
12	Stacked-bar graph used in conjunction with several practice worksheets and quizzes (this handout is in Chapter Three).

HANDOUT 1

Description and Rules

Fantasy Football and Mathematics is a game in which you create and manage a team of players from professional, college, or high school football teams (high school players can select themselves!). Players earn points by scoring touchdowns and two-point conversions and accumulating passing, rushing, and receiving yards. Players lose points for interceptions thrown and fumbles lost. Each week you will find the sum of the points earned by your players. The goal of the game is to accumulate the highest number of points.

How to Select Players

There are two options for selecting players. Your teacher will decide which option your class will be using.

Option 1. You have a salary cap of $40 million to select eleven professional players and two team defenses. Your instructor will provide you with a list of players and their costs. Table 1 lists the number of players selected at each position, as well as the number of players in a starting lineup.

You may select the same players or defensive teams as other students. For example, several students may want to select the same quarterback, which is fine.

Option 2. Each week you select one team. For example, if you live in Atlanta, you may decide to select your hometown team for the first week of the game. However, you may not choose that team in later weeks, because you can select each team only once during the game. Unlike in option 1, you will compute points using team statistics rather than from individual statistics. For example, if your team had a total of 127 yards rushing, you would use that number to compute points.

Table 1. Complete Roster and Starting Lineup Each Week

Position	Number of Players Selected for Each Position	Number of Players Selected for Starting Lineup
Quarterback	2	1
Running back	3	2
Wide receiver (includes tight ends)	4	3
Kicker	2	1
Team defense	2	1

Description and Rules *(Cont'd.)*

It is important for you to select high-scoring teams that are playing against weak opponents in order to maximize the points you will earn. That said, there is as much luck in Fantasy Football as there is skill.

If you use option 1 to select players, your rosters will remain the same for the duration of the game (with the exception of trades, which are explained in the next section). If you use option 2, your players will change every week.

Trades

You may trade players if you selected players using option 1. Trades do not have to be position for position. For example, you might decide to trade a kicker for a quarterback. But in that case, you would have only one kicker. If that kicker got injured, you would not have a kicker in your starting lineup, which is not advised. If you are thinking about making a trade, you need to consider its impact on your full roster. If you do make a trade, it is important that you make the necessary changes to your Fantasy team roster.

Salary cap numbers do not apply to trades.

Injuries and Bye Weeks

If you cannot locate a player's name in the box scores, he is probably injured or the team didn't play that week (this is called a *bye week*). *If this occurs, the players' score is counted as zero.* A player who is placed on injured reserve (IR) will not play for the remainder of the season. If a player is declared out for the year and you used option 1 to select players, you may use the portion of the salary cap you spent on that player to purchase another player. A list of injured players can be found in newspapers as well as online at www.fantasysportsmath.com or other sports Web sites.

HANDOUT 2

Fantasy Team Roster

Name of Fantasy Team: ____________ Team Owner: ____________

Position	Name	Team	Cost
Quarterback			
Quarterback			
Running back			
Running back			
Running back			
Wide receiver			
Wide receiver			
Wide receiver			
Wide receiver			
Kicker			
Kicker			
Team defense			
Team defense			

HANDOUT 3

How to Read Box Scores

Two sections of a fabricated box score are shown below. Box scores are written in several formats. The sections of box scores you will use are usually titled "Scoring Summary" and "Player (or Individual) Statistics." A player (other than a kicker) whose name is listed in the scoring summary has scored a touchdown or passed for a touchdown. (The only exception is a two-point conversion, which occurs when a team elects to try for two points rather than kick the point after a touchdown. On a two-point conversion, a team gets one chance to get the ball in the end zone from the two-yard line.) For example, in Table 1, the first score of the game was a three-yard touchdown run by Aaron Dunlap. Additional touchdowns were scored in the second quarter by Frank Loery, Devan Shalter, Gary Hollings, and Ollie Mays. In addition, Steve Blake and Jesse Wade passed for touchdowns in the second quarter.

Kickers earn points for field goals (FG) and the point after touchdown (PAT). Notice, for example, that Angel Ramos kicked the point after touchdown after the first touchdown of the game. He also kicked a field goal in the first quarter.

Table 1. Sample Box Score: Panthers at Tigers

1ST QUARTER	
TD	Aaron Dunlap, 3 Yd run (Angel Ramos kick is good), 9:59. Drive: 9 plays, 63 yards in 5:01.
FG	Angel Ramos 38 Yd, 2:00. Drive: 8 plays, 76 yards in 4:31.
2ND QUARTER	
TD	Frank Loery, 8 Yd pass from Steve Blake (Angel Ramos kick is good), 13:43. Drive: 6 plays, 27 yards in 3:08.
TD	Devan Shalter, 40 Yd interception return (Henry Darris 2 Pt. Conversion pass to failed), 4:41.
TD	Gary Hollings, 96 Yd kick return (Angel Ramos kick is good), 4:27.
TD	Ollie Mays, 7 Yd pass from Jesse Wade (Brian Martinez kick is good), 1:14. Drive: 5 plays, 50 yards in 1:26.
3RD QUARTER	
FG	Brian Martinez 44 Yd, 12:14. Drive: 8 plays, 26 yards in 2:46.
TD	Mack Knightly, 3 Yd pass from Jesse Wade (Jesse Wade pass to Ty Johnson for 2 Pt. Conversion), 1:54. Drive: 4 plays, 60 yards in 1:41.
4TH QUARTER	
FG	Brian Martinez 37 Yd, 11:38. Drive: 9 plays, 71 yards in 3:49.
TD	D.J. Tucker, 1 Yd pass from Jesse Wade (Brian Martinez kick is good), 8:57. Drive: 6 plays, 25 yards in 2:33.
FG	Brian Martinez 26 Yd, 3:22. Drive: 9 plays, 33 yards in 3:48.
TD	Gary Hollings, 15 Yd pass from Steve Blake (Angel Ramos kick is good), 1:24. Drive: 8 plays, 75 yards in 1:58.

Note: TD = touchdown. FG = field goal.

How to Read Box Scores *(Cont'd.)*

The touchdowns scored by Devan Shalter and Gary Hollings were scored by players on defensive teams. Therefore, students who had the Panthers or Tigers as their defensive team would earn points. Defensive touchdowns are preceded by phrases such as "interception return," "fumble return," "punt return," "kickoff return," or "fumble recovery in end zone." Defensive teams also earn points by safeties, which occur when an offensive player is tackled in his own end zone. Safeties are listed as such and are rare; there were not any safeties in this game.

Players lose points for interceptions thrown and fumbles lost. The box score in Table 2 shows that Jesse Wade threw one interception (INT), and Gary Hollings and Josh Maris each lost one fumble (FUM).

The starting lineup in Table 3 on page 33 is used for reference purposes throughout this book.

Table 2. Box Score: Panthers at Tigers (Week 1)

PASSING—Panthers				
	CP/AT	YDS	TD	INT
J. Wade	33/48	369	3	1
PASSING—Tigers				
	CP/AT	YDS	TD	INT
S. Blake	19/30	221	2	2
RUSHING—Panthers				
	ATT	YDS	TD	LG
T. Johnson	9	15	0	7
L. Jones	4	14	0	8
J. Wade	4	−1	0	2
RUSHING—Tigers				
	ATT	YDS	TD	LG
A. Dunlap	18	84	1	16
J. Maris	7	34	0	21
Y. Ussif	1	23	0	23
S. Blake	1	3	0	3

(Cont'd.)

How to Read Box Scores *(Cont'd.)*

Table 2. Box Score: Panthers at Tigers (Week 1) *(Cont'd)*

RECEIVING—Panthers				
	REC	YDS	TD	LG
O. Mays	11	171	1	30
D. J. Tucker	9	67	1	19
T. Johnson	6	33	0	11
Mack Knightly	7	98	1	31
RECEIVING—Tigers				
	REC	YDS	TD	LG
F. Loery	7	109	1	49
G. Hollings	4	45	1	22
M. Sallinger	1	38	0	38
Y. Ussif	5	24	0	10
T. Faumuina	2	5	0	4
FUMBLES—Panthers				
	FUM	LOST	REC	YDS
C. Vickman	1	1	0	0
FUMBLES—Tigers				
	FUM	LOST	REC	YDS
G. Hollings	1	1	0	0
J. Maris	1	1	0	0
KICKING—Panthers				
	FG	LG	XP	PTS
B. Martinez	3/4	44	2/2	11
KICKING—Tigers				
	FG	LG	XP	PTS
A. Ramos	1/1	38	4/4	7

Note: cp = number of completed passes; at = number of passes attempted; yds = number of yards gained; td = number of touchdowns; int = number of interceptions; att = number of rushing attempts; lg = longest(gain); rec = number of receptions; fum = number of fumbles; lost = number of fumbles lost; rec = number of fumbles recovered; fg = field goal; lg = longest(field goal); xp = number of extra points(or PATs); pts = number of points scored

How to Read Box Scores *(Cont'd.)*

Table 3. Starting Lineup for the Wildcats

Jesse Wade	Quarterback
Ty Johnson	Running back
Josh Maris	Running back
Ollie Mays	Wide receiver
D. J. Tucker	Wide receiver
Tao Faumuina	Wide receiver
Angel Ramos	Kicker
Tigers	Defense

HANDOUT 4

How to Collect Data

Each week, you will use newspapers or online resources to collect data from one game in which each of your players in your starting lineup participated. Accessing data online is the quickest and easiest method. Statistics are also archived online so you can collect data in case you miss a week or two.

Follow these steps to locate statistics online at www.fantasysportsmath.com:

1. Click the "Get Football Stats" link.
2. On the following page, use the calendar to select the week you are looking for.
3. Find a team that one of your players participated in and click on the box score for that game.

HANDOUT 5

How to Compute Points: Default Scoring System

The default scoring system can be used each week to determine the ranking of students' teams in the game. The default scoring system was designed so that you can plot the weekly points earned for your players to precise numerical values on stacked-bar and multiple-line graphs. This is explained later. However, your teacher may choose a different scoring system.

The points that you earn can be computed by two different methods. One method uses algebra, and the other does not.

The non-algebraic method lists touchdowns, two-point conversions, and yards gained for each player. Points are earned for each set of 25 yards gained from passing, as well as each set of 10 yards gained from rushing or receiving. Consequently, yards gained from passing are divided by 25, and yards gained from rushing or receiving are divided by 10. Quotients are always rounded down to the nearest whole number. For example, Jesse Wade passed for 369 yards, which is divided by 25. The quotient of 14.76 is rounded down to 14. Since there are 14 25s in 369, and each 25 yards is worth $\frac{1}{48}$, 14 is multiplied by $\frac{1}{48}$ to arrive at $\frac{14}{48}$. If students cannot multiply fractions, they can use repeated addition to compute points. This process is also used to compute points earned from rushing and receiving yards, with the exception that you compute the number of 10s rather than the number of 25s.

Table 1 uses the non-algebraic method to compute the points for the Wildcats. The points earned have been computed for the first player (Wade). Your task is to complete this worksheet. Compute points for players from the Panthers–Tigers box score in Handout 3.

The second method of computing points uses algebra; it uses equations that contain variables. These equations are known as *total points equations* because they are used to compute the total points for one week for all players, with the exception of kickers and team defenses.

How to Compute Points: Default Scoring System *(Cont'd.)*

For Each:	Players Earn:
Kickers	
Point after touchdown (PAT)	$\frac{1}{48}$ or .021
Field goal (FG)	$\frac{1}{16}$ or .063
Quarterbacks, running backs, wide receivers, defenses	
Touchdown (by passing, rushing, or receiving)	$\frac{1}{8}$ or .125
Two point conversion	$\frac{1}{24}$ or .042
Touchdown by a defense	$\frac{1}{8}$ or .125
Safety by a defense	$\frac{1}{24}$ or .042
Interception	$-\frac{1}{12}$ or −.083
Fumble	$-\frac{1}{16}$ or −.063
Passing yards	$\frac{1}{48}$ for every 25 yards
Rushing or receiving yards	$\frac{1}{48}$ for every 10 yards

Note: Decimals are rounded to the nearest thousandth.

HANDOUT 6

Practice in Computing Points Using the Default Scoring System

Use the following chart to compute points for the players listed in the Panthers-Tigers box score.

	Wade	Johnson	Maris	Mays	Tucker	Faumuina	Ramos	Tigers
Number of TDs $\times \frac{1}{8}$	$\frac{3}{8}$							
Number of 2-point conversions or safeties $\times \frac{1}{24}$	$\frac{1}{24}$							
Number of passing yards (in 25s) $\times \frac{1}{48}$	$\frac{14}{48}$							
Number of rushing yards (in 10s) $\times \frac{1}{48}$	0							
Number of receiving yards (in 10s) $\times \frac{1}{48}$	0							
Number of PATs $\times \frac{1}{48}$	0							
Number of FGs $\times \frac{1}{16}$	0							
Number of interceptions $\times \left(-\frac{1}{12}\right)$	$-\frac{1}{12}$							
Number of fumbles lost $\times \left(-\frac{1}{16}\right)$	0							
Total individual points:	$\frac{30}{48}$							
Total team points:	$\frac{30}{48}+$							

HANDOUT 7

Default Total Points Equation

In this equation, which is used for quarterbacks, running backs, and wide receivers, the numerical values are the same as the default scoring system:

$$\frac{1}{8}(T) + \frac{1}{24}(V) + \frac{1}{48}(P + R + C) - \frac{1}{12}(I) - \frac{1}{16}(F) = W$$

T = number of touchdowns scored by passing, rushing, or receiving
V = number of two-point conversions scored by passing, rushing, or receiving
P = number of passing yards divided by 25, then rounded down to the nearest whole number
R = number of rushing yards divided by 10, then rounded down to the nearest whole number
C = number of receiving yards divided by 10, then rounded down to the nearest whole number
I = number of interceptions thrown
F = number of fumbles lost
W = total points scored for one week for one individual player

HANDOUT 8

Practice in Computing Points Using the Default Total Points Equation

$$\frac{1}{8}(T) + \frac{1}{24}(V) + \frac{1}{48}(P + R + C) - \frac{1}{12}(I) - \frac{1}{16}(F) = W$$

Use Handout 3 to fill out the following table.

Player	Computation	Points
Wade	$\frac{1}{8}(3) + \frac{1}{24}(1) + \frac{1}{48}(14 + 0 + 0) - \frac{1}{12}(1) - \frac{1}{16}(0) = W$	
Johnson		
Maris		
Mays		
Tucker		
Faumuina		

Peer Signature: ______________________________

HANDOUT 9

Weekly Scoring Worksheet (Week ____)

Fill in the numerical values for scoring criteria in the left column. If you are using the default scoring system, the numerical values are listed on Handout 5. If you are using a different scoring system, your teacher will tell you the numerical values. You can get the statistics you need to fill out this handout at www.fantasysportsmath.com.

	QB	RB 1	RB 2	WR 1	WR 2	WR 3	K	Def
Number of TDs × ______								
Number of two-point conversions or safeties × ______								
Number of passing yards (in 25s) × ______								
Number of rushing yards (in 10s) × ______								
Number of receiving yards (in 10s) × ______								
Number of PATs × ______								
Number of FGs × ______								
Number of interceptions × ______								
Number of fumbles lost × ______								
Total individual points								
Total points for the week:								

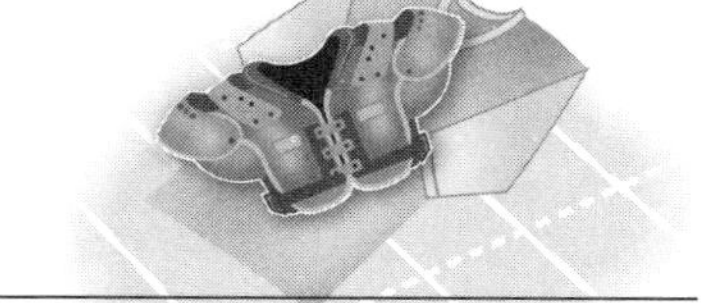

Peer Signature: 

HANDOUT 10

Weekly Scoring Worksheet Using Total Points Equations (Week ____)

Total points equations are not used to compute points for kickers and defenses. Write the total points equation you are using in the box below. Then compute the points for each of your players. You can get the statistics you need to fill out this handout at www.fantasysportsmath.com.

Player	Computation	Points
QB		
RB1		
WR1		
WR2		
WR3		
K		
Defense		
Total points for the week:		

HANDOUT 11

Total Points Week-by-Week

Team Name: ______________________ Student Name: ______________________

Week	QB	RB	RB	WR	WR	WR	K	Def	Weekly Total	Cumulative Total
1										
2										
3										
4										
5										
6										
7										
8										

Total Points Week-by-Week *(Cont'd.)*

Team Name: ______________________ Student Name: ______________________

Week	QB	RB	RB	WR	WR	WR	K	Def	Weekly Total	Cumulative Total
9										
10										
11										
12										
13										
14										
15										
16										
17										

Part Two

Using Graphs

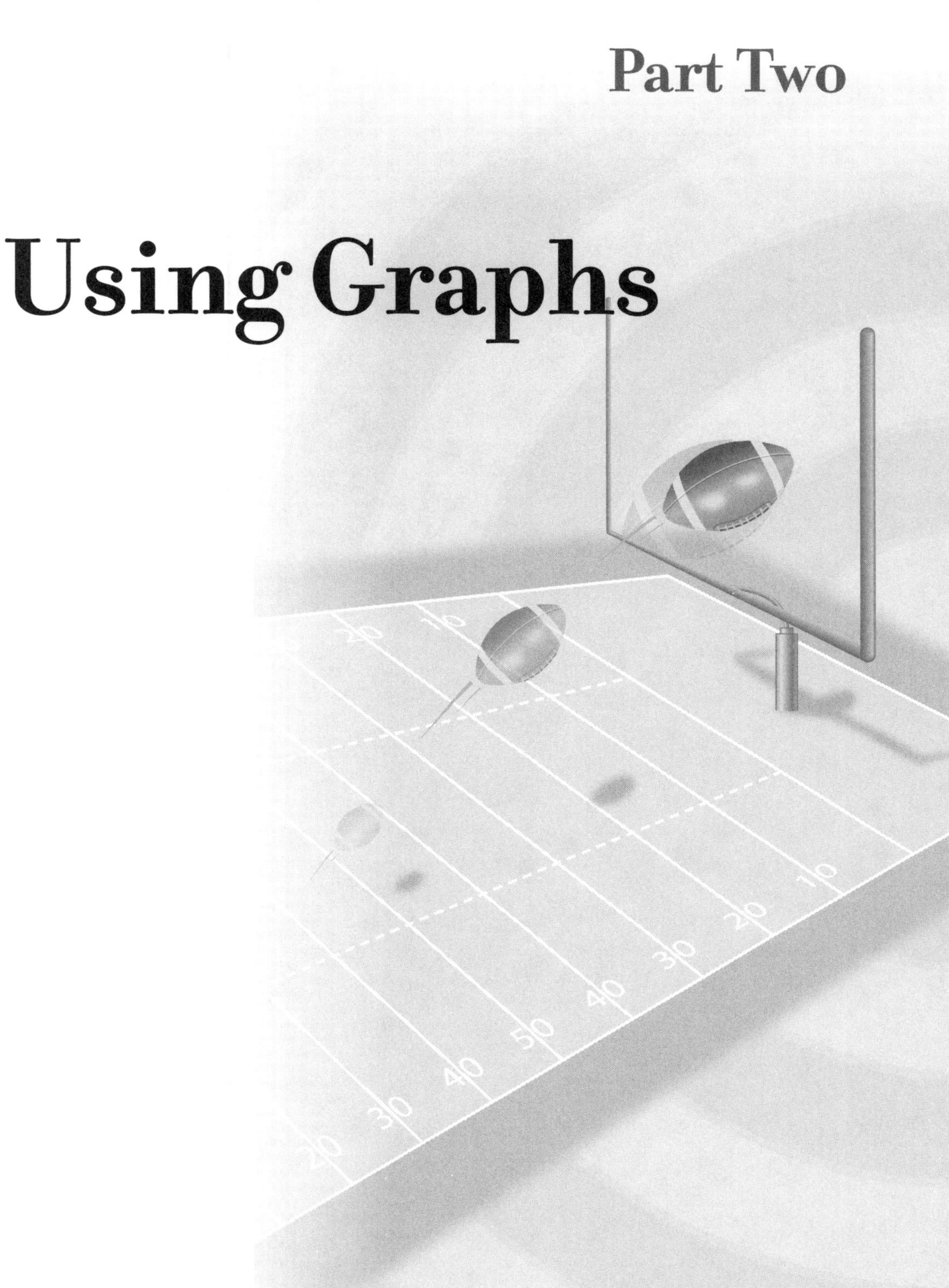

Chapter Three

Graphing Activities

Students construct circle, stacked-bar, or multiple-line graphs that reflect the performance of their teams. Students may create one or several graphs each week, depending on their skills. Although the graphs in this chapter are computer generated, I highly recommend that students construct their graphs by hand so they can perform the computations themselves instead of relying on computer programs to perform the computations for them.

Circle Graphs

Circle graphs indicate the percentage of the fantasy team's points that each player earns. The equation for computing the measurement of a central angle of a player's portion of the circle is as follows:

$$W \div S \times 360 = A$$

W = total weekly points for one player
S = total weekly points for the team
A = the measurement of the central angle on the circle graph

Figure 3.1. Circle Graph

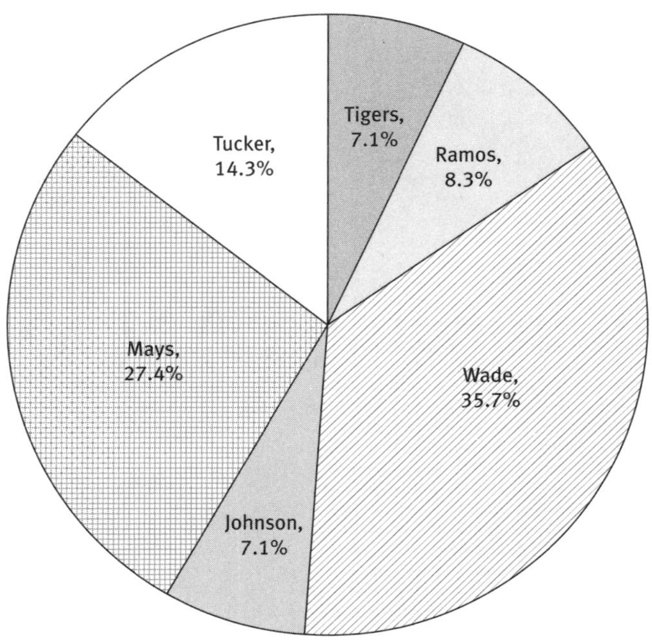

Wildcats Scoring Breakdown, Week 1

Example:

Jesse Wade's total points for week 1 (in simplest form): $\frac{5}{8}$

Total points for the Wildcats for Week 1 (in simplest form): $1\frac{3}{4}$

Step 1: $\frac{5}{8} \div 1\frac{3}{4} = \frac{5}{8} \div \frac{7}{4}$

Step 2: $\frac{5}{8} \div \frac{7}{4} = \frac{5}{8} \times \frac{4}{7}$

Step 3: $\frac{5}{8} \times \frac{4}{7} = \frac{20}{56} = \frac{5}{14} = .357$ (rounded to nearest 1,000th)

Step 4: $.357 \times 360 = 128.52°$, which rounds to 129°

Figure 3.1 shows a circle graph of the points breakdown for the Wildcats in week 1.

Stacked-Bar and Multiple-Line Graphs

Points earned by individual players can be shown on stacked-bar graphs and multiple-line graphs. A stacked-bar graph is one in which players' weekly points are "stacked" on top of each other. Multiple-line graphs are line graphs that depict the weekly points earned by two or more players. Examples of these graphs are found on the following pages. Intervals of $\frac{1}{48}$, $\frac{2}{48}$, or $\frac{4}{48}$ work well for these graphs, assuming students are using the default scoring system. Students may need to tape additional sheets of graph paper to the top of their first sheet in order to accommodate weeks in which their team scores significant points. My students constructed their graphs by hand, and I gave them extra credit if they created computer-generated charts.

The following pages contain examples of computer-generated graphs. Note that the stacked-bar graph is also used as a handout; its data is used as the basis for activities on several Practice Worksheets.

HANDOUT 12

Stacked-Bar Graph

Week 1 Week 2 Week 3 Week 4 Week 5 Week 6

W : Wade M : Maris T : Tucker R : Ramos
J : Johnson O.M. : Mays F : Faumuina Ti : Tigers

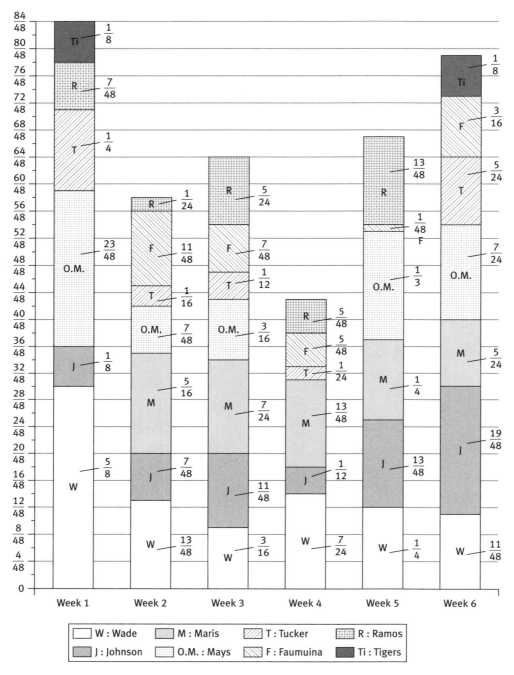

Wildcats Scoring Breakdown, Weeks 1–6

Multiple-Line Graph

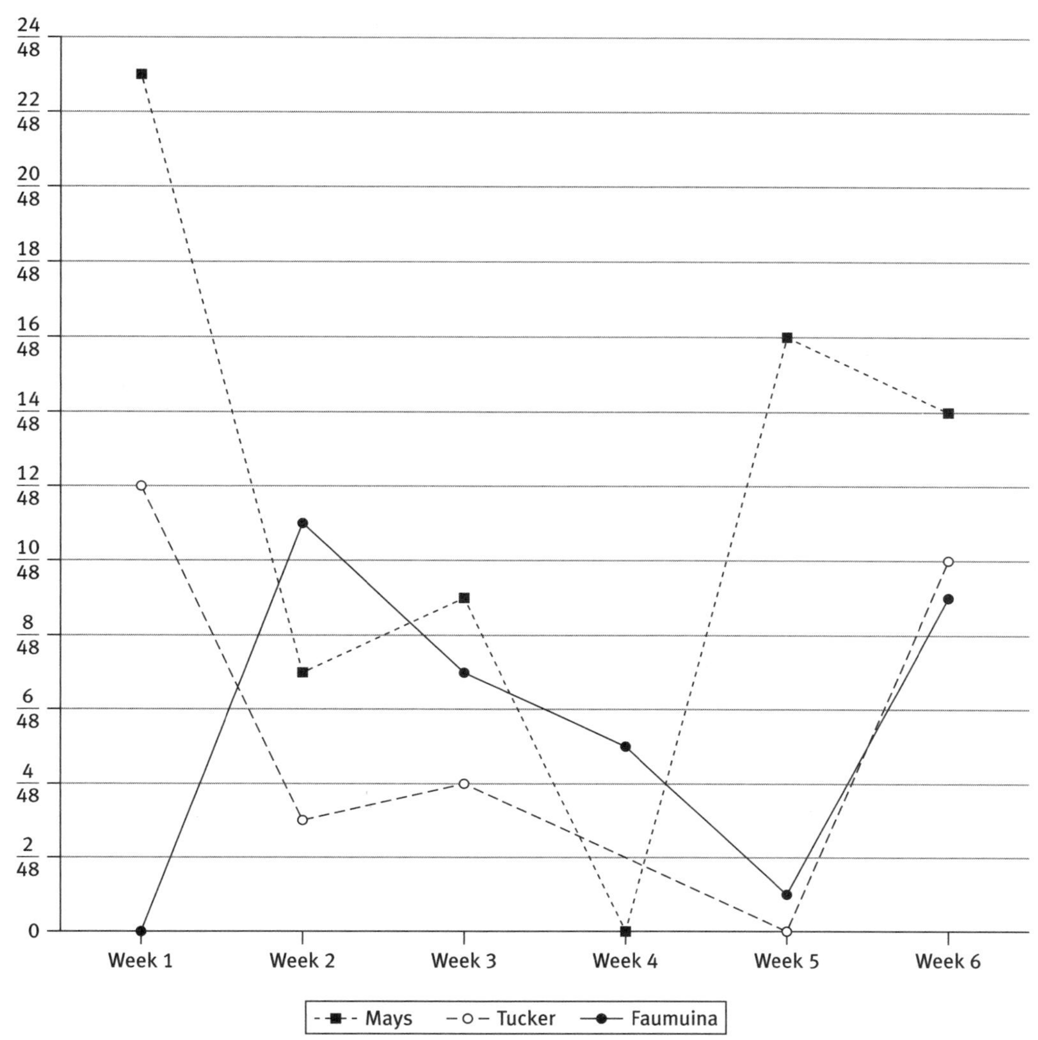

Wildcats Scoring Breakdown, Weeks 1–6

Additional Options for Graphing Activities

- Graph all players' total points for one week on a non-stacked-bar graph in which each player is represented by his own column. Students can construct a new bar graph each week.
- Break down a stacked-bar graph according to positive and negative points earned. For each week, there would be two columns for each player: one column for the positive points (points earned) and another column for the negative points (points lost). The two columns could be next to each other, or the positive column could be above the *x*-axis and the negative column below the *x*-axis. (The second choice is also an option for multiple-line graphs.)
- Select one or more scoring categories to graph. (This also works well for multiple-line graphs.) For instance, students could choose to graph passing yards gained, rushing yards gained, or total yards gained. Students need to select appropriate intervals for the *y*-axis. Giving students opportunities to select appropriate intervals allows them to use higher-level thinking skills.

Part Three

Using Practice Worksheets and Quizzes

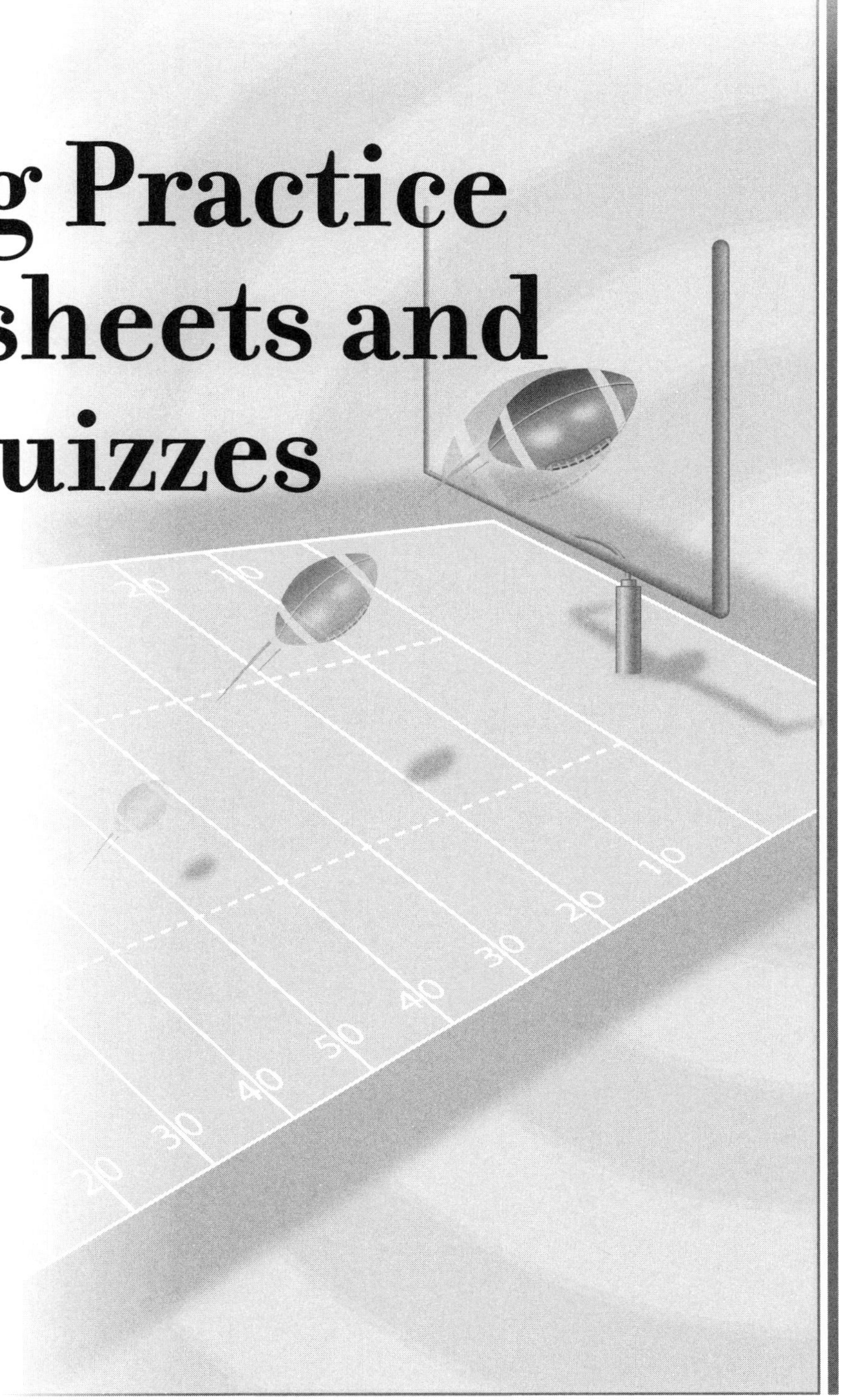

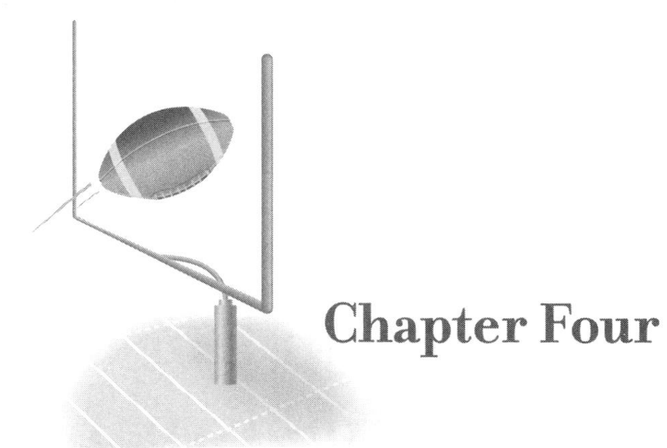

Chapter Four

Practice Worksheets

Practice worksheets from this book can be integrated into your existing curriculum in order to maximize the thematic approach to mathematics that the game provides. For example, if students are learning how to round decimals, you can use the corresponding worksheet in this text, in which students round the decimal equivalents for the points earned by their players. Consequently, students will be presented with opportunities to reinforce math concepts that tie in with the game. This approach will help students to make connections between math in school and math in the real world.

Each week, one or more worksheets may be integrated into your math lessons. Some worksheets (for example, Practice Worksheet 40: Mean, Median, Mode, Range) can be used for several weeks because students perform operations based on the points earned by their players for a given week. Other worksheets are used to compute cumulative points earned for the first few weeks of the season. These worksheets have a cumulative effect because students receive multiple exposures to the same material on a weekly basis. As the season progresses, students may work on several worksheets each week. Multiple exposures to content also facilitates mastery. For these reasons, it is highly recommended that students also participate in the graphing activities, for weekly exposures to circle, stacked-bar, and multiple-line graphs will help them to comprehend the material.

Students can also create their own worksheets based on their team's performance. For instance, if students are learning how to add and subtract fractions, they can write problems based on the points earned by their players—for example, "If player A earned three-eighths and player B earned four-fifths, how many total points did they earn?"

Name ____

PRACTICE WORKSHEET 1

Rounding Whole Numbers and Expanded Notation

1. Round the following player salaries to the units given. The first line gives an example.

Salary	***Nearest $10,000***	***Nearest $100,000***	***Nearest $1,000,000***
$4,884,650	4,880,000	4,900,000	5,000,000
$5,009,900			
$3,555,555			
$2,999,009			
$4,103,737			

2. Use expanded notation to represent the following player salaries. The first line gives an example.

Salary

$6,675,505 = 6,000,000 + 600,000 + 70,000 + 5,000 + 500 + 5

$4,884,650

$5,009,900

$3,555,555

$2,999,009

$4,103,737

Name ____

PRACTICE WORKSHEET 2

Least Common Multiple and Greatest Common Factor

The weekly points scored by a team for one season are listed below. Find the least common multiple and greatest common factor for each pair of numbers. The first line gives an example.

Weeks	***Points Scored***	***Least Common Multiple***	***Greatest Common Factor***
Weeks 1, 2	7, 21	21	7
Weeks 3, 4	35, 5		
Weeks 5, 6	21, 5		
Weeks 7, 8	10, 30		
Weeks 9, 10	45, 9		

Name ____

PRACTICE WORKSHEET 3

Operations with Whole Numbers

1. What is the difference between the most expensive and least expensive players listed below?

Player A	$14,007,924
Player B	$14,950,351
Player C	$14,800,995
Player D	$14,675,228
Player E	$14,650,774
Player F	$14,425,005
Player G	$ 3,777,902

2. What is the total cost of the players listed in question 1?

3. What is the average cost of the players listed in question 1, to the nearest dollar?

4. If a player rushed for 1,364 yards in 10 games, how many yards did he average per game?

5. If 14 players each have a salary of $2.7 million, what is the sum of their salaries?

Name ____

PRACTICE WORKSHEET 4

Equivalent Fractions

The points earned by players on the Wildcats are listed below. List the first three equivalent fractions for each.

Jesse Wade	$\frac{5}{8}$	$\frac{10}{16}$	$\frac{15}{24}$	$\frac{20}{32}$
Ty Johnson	$\frac{7}{16}$	____	____	____
Josh Maris	$\frac{2}{3}$	____	____	____
Ollie Mays	$\frac{1}{4}$	____	____	____
D. J. Tucker	$\frac{3}{8}$	____	____	____
Tao Faumuina	$\frac{5}{24}$	____	____	____
Angel Ramos	$\frac{5}{6}$	____	____	____

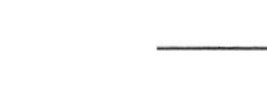

Name ____

PRACTICE WORKSHEET 5

Patterns and Multiples

(Use with Handout 12)

1. Find the first three multiples for the points Jesse Wade earned for week 5. Reduce fractions to simplest form.

2. Find the first three multiples for the points Ty Johnson earned for week 4. Reduce fractions to simplest form.

3. Find the first three multiples for the points earned by Josh Maris for week 2. Reduce fractions to simplest form.

4. If $\frac{60}{48}$ is the third multiple of a number, what is the original number?

5. If 6 is the fourth multiple of a number, what is the original number?

Name ______________________________

PRACTICE WORKSHEET 6

Ordering Fractions and Decimals

(Use with Handout 12)

Example

For week 6, use inequalities to arrange the points earned by players on the Wildcats in ascending order.

$$\frac{6}{48} < \frac{9}{48} < \frac{10}{48} < \frac{10}{48} < \frac{11}{48} < \frac{14}{48} < \frac{19}{48}$$

After converting the fractions to decimals and rounding to the nearest thousandth, you can arrange the decimals in descending order:

$$.396 > .292 > .229 > .208 \geq .208 > .188 > .125$$

Use inequalities to arrange the points earned by players on the Wildcats in descending order for the following weeks. Round decimals to the nearest thousandth.

Week 1

Week 2

Week 3

Week 4

Week 5

Name ____

PRACTICE WORKSHEET 7

Rounding Decimals

(Use with Handout 12)

Round each player's cumulative points from weeks 1–6 to the nearest tenth, hundredth, and thousandth.

Example

Jesse Wade's cumulative points for Weeks 1–6: $\frac{89}{48} = 1\frac{41}{48} = 1.8541$

Round to the nearest tenth = 1.9

Round to the nearest hundredth = 1.85

Round to the nearest thousandth = 1.854

Table 1

	Johnson	Maris	Mays	Tucker	Faumuina	Ramos	Tigers
Total Points in Weeks 1–6 (Fraction)							
Total Points in Weeks 1–6 (Decimal)							
Nearest Tenth							
Nearest Hundredth							
Nearest Thousandth							

Use the following table to round the cumulative points for your players for weeks 1–6.

Table 2

Total Points in Weeks 1–6 (Fraction)							
Total Points in Weeks 1–6 (Decimal)							
Nearest Tenth							
Nearest Hundredth							
Nearest Thousandth							

Name ____

PRACTICE WORKSHEET 8

Improper Fractions, Mixed Numbers, and Reciprocals

The weekly point totals for a team are listed below. Convert all improper fractions to mixed numbers, and write each in its simplest form.

Example

$$\frac{66}{48} = 1\frac{18}{48} = 1\frac{3}{8}$$

1. $\frac{79}{48}$

2. $\frac{38}{48}$

3. $\frac{50}{48}$

4. $\frac{106}{48}$

5. $\frac{66}{48}$

Write the reciprocals (in simplest form) of the original fractions given in problems 1–5.

6.

7.

8.

9.

10.

Name ____

PRACTICE WORKSHEET 9

Adding and Subtracting Fractions

(Use with Handout 12)

Example

For week 5, find the sum of the points earned by Josh Maris, Ollie Mays, and Tao Faumuina.

$$\frac{12}{48} + \frac{16}{48} + \frac{1}{48} = \frac{29}{48}$$

1. For week 3, find the sum of the points earned by Jesse Wade, Ty Johnson, and Ollie Mays.

2. For week 2, find the sum of the points earned by the Wildcats, with the exception of Angel Ramos and Josh Maris.

3. Find the sum of the points earned by Ollie Mays and Jesse Wade for weeks 1–5.

4. Find the sum of the points earned by all players for weeks 1–3, with the exception of Jesse Wade and Ollie Mays.

5. For week 4, find the sum of the points earned by all players, with the exception of Ty Johnson and Angel Ramos.

Name ______________________________

PRACTICE WORKSHEET 10

Stacked-Bar Graphs

(Use with Handout 12)

Using graph paper and an interval of $\frac{4}{48}$, construct a stacked-bar graph based on the data below. *Hint:* Convert all fractions so that they have a common denominator.

Player	***Week 1***	***Week 2***	***Week 3***
QB	$\frac{5}{12}$	$\frac{1}{2}$	$\frac{29}{48}$
RB	$\frac{7}{16}$	$\frac{19}{48}$	$\frac{5}{12}$
WR	$\frac{1}{16}$	$\frac{1}{3}$	$\frac{3}{8}$

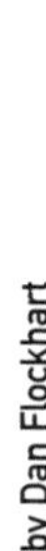

Name ____

PRACTICE WORKSHEET 11

Multiplying and Dividing Fractions

1. How many weeks would it take a player to earn $5\frac{33}{48}$ points if he averaged $\frac{7}{16}$ points a week?

2. If D. J. Tucker earned $\frac{1}{16}$ points and Ollie Mays earned $\frac{7}{48}$ points, what is the product of their points earned?

3. The product of the points that Jesse Wade and Ollie Mays earned is $\frac{27}{128}$. If Wade earned $\frac{9}{16}$ points, how many points did Mays earn?

4. A player earned $12\frac{16}{48}$ points during a 16-game season. How many points did he average per week?

5. If Marvin Samuels earned $2\frac{1}{8}$ points for the season, and Reggie Blackmon earned $\frac{7}{16}$ for each week, how many weeks would it take Blackmon to match Samuels's points?

Name ____________________

PRACTICE WORKSHEET 12

Rounding Fractions

(Use with Handout 12)

1. In Table 1, round the players' cumulative points from weeks 1–6 to the nearest $\frac{1}{2}$, $\frac{1}{4}$, and $\frac{1}{8}$.

Example

Ollie Mays's cumulative points for weeks 1–6 $= \frac{69}{48} = 1\frac{21}{48} = 1\frac{7}{16}$

Round to the nearest $\frac{1}{2} = 1\frac{1}{2}$

Round to the nearest $\frac{1}{4} = 1\frac{1}{2}$

Round to the nearest $\frac{1}{8} = 1\frac{1}{2}$

Table 1

	Wade	Johnson	Maris	Tucker	Faumuina	Ramos	Tigers
Nearest $\frac{1}{2}$							
Nearest $\frac{1}{4}$							
Nearest $\frac{1}{8}$							

Use the following table to round the cumulative points for your players for weeks 1–6.

Table 2

Player							
Nearest $\frac{1}{2}$							
Nearest $\frac{1}{4}$							
Nearest $\frac{1}{8}$							

Name ____

PRACTICE WORKSHEET 13

Multiplying and Dividing Decimals

1. If a quarterback had annual quarterback ratings of 88.64, 101.88, 76.75, 90.09, and 93.53, what would be his average rating for the past five years?

2. If Doug Jones worked 8 hours a day, 175 days a year, and his annual salary was $4.4 million, how much money did he make each working day? Each working hour? Each working minute? Each working second? Round your answers to the nearest cent.

3. If a snail can crawl at a rate of .07 yards per minute, how many hours will it take the snail to crawl the length of a football field (100 yards)? One mile?

4. If 60,000 fans each consumed an average of 7.75 ounces of soda at each game, how many ounces of soda were consumed for 14 games? How many 12 ounce sodas were consumed?

5. If a vendor selling ice cream sandwiches works 4 hours at $7.50 an hour and also receives 35 cents for each sandwich sold, what is her income if she sold 323 sandwiches?

Name ____

PRACTICE WORKSHEET 14

Unit Rates

Example

At a football game, you can purchase 16 ounces of soda for \$2.75 or 24 ounces for \$4.00. Which size is the lower price per ounce?

\$2.75 ÷ 16 ounces = 17.2 cents per ounce

\$4.00 ÷ 24 ounces = 16.7 cents per ounce (lowest price per ounce)

The 24-ounce size has the lower price per ounce.

1. If you can purchase 12 ounces of peanuts for \$3.75 or 20 ounces for \$5.75, what is the cost for the lower price per ounce?

2. If Susan Haines drove her car 300 miles on 30 gallons of gas and Chrissy Dolling drove her car 450 miles on 15 gallons of gas, what is the miles per gallon for each car?

3. If Jessica Williams can purchase 50 acres for \$2.5 million or 75 acres for \$3.5 million, what is the cost of the lower price per acre?

4. If you can purchase a 10-game season ticket for \$450 or a 1-game ticket for \$55, which is the lower price per game?

5. Which is the higher salary per year: \$4.5 million for 8 years or \$8.5 million for 15 years?

Name ____

PRACTICE WORKSHEET 15

Converting Fractions, Decimals, and Percentages

(Use with Handout 12)

1. Find the cumulative points for each player, and convert the fractions into decimals. Then round to the nearest tenth, hundredth, and thousandth. Finally, convert all decimals to a percentage, rounded to the nearest tenth.

Player	Total Points (Fraction)	Total Points (Decimal)	Rounded to Nearest Tenth	Rounded to Nearest Hundredth	Rounded to Nearest Thousandth	Percentage (Rounded to Nearest Tenth)
Wade	$1\frac{41}{48}$	1.8542	1.9	1.85	1.854	185.4%
Johnson						
Maris						
Mays						
Tucker						

2. Fill in the table below for the cumulative points for your team for the first six weeks.

Your Player	Total Points (Fraction)	Total Points (Decimal)	Rounded to Nearest Tenth	Rounded to Nearest Hundredth	Rounded to Nearest Thousandth	Percentage (Rounded to Nearest Tenth)
QB						
RB1						
RB2						
WR1						
WR2						
WR3						

Name ____

PRACTICE WORKSHEET 16

Ratios

(Use with Handout 12)

Example

$$\frac{\text{Total points for Mays, Tucker, and Faumuina}}{\text{Total points for Wade}} = \frac{17}{12} = 1.41\overline{6} = 141.7\%$$

For week 5, find the following ratios, and convert them to percentages.

1. $\dfrac{\text{Total points for Johnson and Maris}}{\text{Total points for Mays, Tucker, and Faumuina}}$

2. $\dfrac{\text{Total points for Wade}}{\text{Total points for Ramos}}$

3. $\dfrac{\text{Total points for Ramos, Tigers, Johnson, and Maris}}{\text{Total points for Mays, Tucker, Faumuina, and Wade}}$

For week 6, find the following ratios, and convert them to percentages.

4. $\dfrac{\text{Total points for Johnson, Maris, and Ramos}}{\text{Total points for Wade, Mays, Tucker, and Faumunia}}$

5. $\dfrac{\text{Total points for Mays, Tucker, and Faumuina}}{\text{Total points for Johnson and Maris}}$

Name ____

PRACTICE WORKSHEET 17

Percentage of Price Increase and Decrease

Example

If the price of a football jersey rose from \$42 to \$54, what is the percentage of price increase?

$$\frac{\text{Change in Price}}{\text{Original Price}} = \frac{12}{42} = 19.8\% \text{ increase}$$

1. If the price of an autographed football rose from \$155 to \$225, what is the percentage of price increase?

2. If the price of a football video game decreased from \$85 to \$75, what is the percentage of price decrease?

3. If the price of a season ticket decreased from \$675 to \$555, what is the percentage of price decrease?

4. If the price of a season ticket increased from \$465 to \$770, what is the percentage of price increase?

5. If a player's salary increased from \$13 million to \$16.5 million, what percentage increase would that represent?

Name ____

PRACTICE WORKSHEET 18

Finding a Percentage of a Number

Example

Ollie Mays earned $\frac{7}{48}$ points. What percentage of André Young's points $(\frac{15}{48})$ does this represent?

$$n \times \left(\frac{15}{48}\right) = \frac{7}{48}$$

$$\text{therefore, } n = \frac{7}{48} \div \left(\frac{15}{48}\right)$$

$$\text{thus, } n = \frac{7}{15} = .4\overline{6} = 47\%$$

1. Tim Dunfield earned $\frac{6}{48}$ points. What percentage of Larue Jones's points $(\frac{18}{48})$ does this represent?

2. Drew Lane earned $\frac{7}{48}$ points. What percentage of Edgar Palmer's points $(\frac{13}{48})$ does this represent?

3. What percentage of Dan Banning's points $(\frac{31}{48})$ do Greg Foster's points $(\frac{13}{48})$ represent?

4. Curt Brock earned $\frac{16}{48}$ points, which was 80% of Michael Smith's points. How many points did Smith earn?

5. Jesse Wade earned $\frac{1}{8}$ points, which was 60% of Ollie Mays's points. How many points did Mays earn?

Finding a Percentage of a Number *(Cont'd.)*

6. Rod Blanchard earned $\frac{3}{4}$ points, which was 120% of Kevan Williams's points. How many points did Williams earn?

7. If Mike Dillion earned 150% of his week 8 point total ($\frac{6}{48}$), how many points did he earn?

8. There are 80,000 football fans in Oakland and 56,000 baseball fans in San Francisco. Each year, 20% of the football fans move to San Francisco, and 15% of the baseball fans move to Oakland. Complete the table below.

After Year	Baseball Fans in Oakland	Football Fans in San Francisco
1		
2		
3		
4		

Name ____________________

PRACTICE WORKSHEET 19

Proportions

Example

If a player earned $1\frac{6}{24}$ points during the first 4 weeks of the season, how many points is he projected to earn for an entire 16-game season?

$$\frac{1.25}{4} = \frac{n}{16}$$

$$1.25(16) = 4n$$

$$n = 5$$

1. If a player earned $1\frac{5}{16}$ points during the first 7 weeks of the season, how many points is he projected to earn in a 16-game season?

2. If it took a player 3 weeks to earn $\frac{7}{16}$ points, how many weeks would it take him to earn $4\frac{1}{8}$ points?

3. If it took a player 12 weeks to earn $2\frac{1}{48}$ points, how many weeks would it take him to earn 10 points?

4. A player earned $2\frac{8}{12}$ points for the entire season. If he earned an equal number of points each week, how many points did he accumulate after 9 weeks?

Proportions *(Cont'd.)*

5. A player earned 2 points for the entire season. If he earned an equal number of points each week, how many points would he have accumulated after 7 weeks?

6. If a player threw for 1,434 yards during the first 5 games, then how many passing yards is he projected to accumulate in a 16-game season?

7. A player gained 357 yards rushing during the first 3 games. If he maintains his current pace, how many rushing yards will he accumulate through 10 games?

8. An architect is constructing a scale drawing of a new stadium. On the scale, 1 inch represents 20 feet. If the actual length of the football field is 300 feet, what is the length of the football field on the scale drawing?

9. In problem 8, what would be the actual height of the goal posts if the scale drawing showed a height of 2 inches?

10. If it took 33 hours to drive 2,000 miles nonstop, how long would it take to drive 3,000 miles nonstop assuming that the average speed remained constant on both trips?

Name ____

PRACTICE WORKSHEET 20

Ratios and Proportions

Example

During week 4, the ratio of Ron Harris's points to Ben Willis's points was 3:1. If Harris earned $\frac{21}{48}$ points that week, how many points did Willis earn?

$$\frac{3}{1} = \frac{\frac{21}{48}}{n}$$

$$3n = \frac{21}{48}$$

$$n = \frac{7}{48}$$

1. During week 14, the ratio of Jeff McQueen's points to Trey Williamson's points was 4:3. If Williamson earned $\frac{12}{48}$ points, how many points did McQueen earn?

2. During week 12, the ratio of Cory Chavas's points to Tony Packney's points was 1:3. If Packney earned $\frac{24}{48}$ points, how many points did Chavas earn?

3. During week 13, the ratio of Ollie Mays's points to Jesse Wade's points was 5:2. If Mays earned $\frac{30}{48}$ points, how many points did Wade earn?

4. During week 14, the ratio of David Benson's points to Jim Price's points was 6:5. If Price earned $\frac{25}{48}$, how many points did Benson earn?

5. During week 10, the ratio of Jerry Gates's points to Chris Jillian's points was 13:21. If Jillian earned $\frac{7}{8}$ points, how many points did Gates earn?

Name ____

PRACTICE WORKSHEET 21

Factoring

Example

The product of the points earned by Harry Rincot for weeks 1 and 2 is $\frac{18}{48}$. If Rincot earned $\frac{3}{12}$ points for week 1, how many points did he earn for week 2?

$$\frac{3}{12} \times \frac{\square}{\square} = \frac{18}{48}$$

$$n = \frac{6}{4} = 1\frac{1}{2}$$

1. The product of the points earned by two players for week 8 is $\frac{44}{48}$. If one player earned $\frac{11}{12}$ points, how many points did the second player earn?

2. With the exception of 1, find two factors whose product equals $1\frac{18}{48}$.

3. The area of a table tennis table is 45 square feet. If the length and width are whole numbers, what are the only two realistic factors for the table's dimensions?

4. One factor of $\frac{32}{45}$ is $\frac{4}{9}$. Find a second factor.

5. Find a second factor if one factor of $\frac{24}{48}$ is 4.

Name ____

PRACTICE WORKSHEET 22

Interest, Depreciation, and Tax

1. If a player signed an eight-year contract for $105,000,000 and invested 45% of his annual salary at a rate of 6.25% for each year, how much interest will he earn at the end of 2 years if the interest is compounded annually? (Assume that his income remains constant during the life of the contract.) Construct a spreadsheet showing the interest earned and total value of his account at the end of each year. Use the following formula:

   I = PRT
   I = interest earned
   P = principle
   R = interest rate
   T = time

2. If a player purchases a car for $150,000, and the state sales tax rate is 8.5%, how much tax will he owe? What will be the total cost of the car?

3. If the value of the automobile depreciates by 10% each year, what will the car be worth at the end of 3 years? Construct a spreadsheet showing the amount of depreciation and corresponding value of the car each year.

4. If a player purchased a house for $8,500,000, and the price of the home appreciates 10% a year for the next 2 years, what will be the value of the home at the end of that period? Construct a spreadsheet showing the amount of annual appreciation and corresponding value of the house at the end of each year.

Name ____

PRACTICE WORKSHEET 23

Prime Factorization

Below are the weekly point totals (in 48ths) for a team. Write the prime factorization of each number using exponential notation. The first row is filled in as an example.

Week	*Point Totals*	*Prime Factorization*
Week 1	66	$2 \times 3 \times 11$
Week 2	79	
Week 3	38	
Week 4	50	
Week 5	106	
Week 6	66	
Week 7	69	

List the first five prime numbers: ____ ____ ____ ____ ____

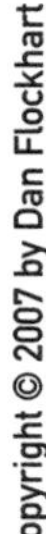

Name ____

PRACTICE WORKSHEET 24

Scientific Notation

The dimensions of a football field are 300 feet by 160 feet. Write the area of the field in scientific notation for the following units of measurement. *Hint*: 1 in. = 2.5 cm.

Example

Square feet   Area = 48,000 sq. feet = 4.8×10^4

1. Square inches
2. Square yards
3. Square centimeters
4. Square millimeters
5. Square meters
6. 26.75
7. .000005
8. .000777
9. 877,887.5665
10. 1,000,000.7

Write the following in standard form.

11. 9.002×10^{-2}
12. $\frac{15}{48} \times 10^3$

Name ____________________

PRACTICE WORKSHEET 25

Ordering Integers, Fractions, and Decimals

1. The following integers represent the temperatures for several cities in December. Place them in ascending order on the number line below.

   45 −3 −21 −17 −9 −32 21 76 44 −1 11

   ____

2. The following integers represent the rushing yards gained or lost by a quarterback during the first 10 games of the season. Place them in ascending order on the number line below.

   −34 12 7 21 −55 −33 −3 −41 41 −2

   ____

3. Place the following numerical values on the number line in ascending order.

   $-.011998$ $4\frac{2}{5}$ $-5\frac{5}{16}$ -2.888 7.004 $-3\frac{7}{8}$

   ____

4. Place the following numerical values on the number line in ascending order.

   $.125$ $\frac{1}{3}$ $\frac{11}{48}$ $\frac{7}{48}$ $\frac{3}{16}$ $\frac{1}{6}$

   ____

Name ____

PRACTICE WORKSHEET 26

Operations with Integers

1. If a quarterback lost 5,553 yards rushing over the course of 15 seasons, how many yards did he lose on average per season?

2. The numerical values below represent the rushing totals for 10 running backs. How many total yards did they rush for?

   −16 126 −3 19 167 −22 −41 −5 −33 65

3. If a running back rushed for −13 yards in the first game of the season, how many yards is he projected to lose for a complete 16-game season?

4. If Tony Reno gained 112 yards in the first game of the season, how many yards is he projected to gain for a complete 16-game season?

Operations with Integers *(Cont'd.)*

5. The numbers below represent profit or loss for five teams for one year. What is the average profit or loss?

   −$445,000 $4,987,435   −$3,722,256   −$66,773 $25,776,232

6. If one team lost $1,978,330 while another team reported a profit of $22,656,944, how much greater was the second team's profit compared to the other team's loss?

7. If one team reported a loss of $13,111,008, which included a profit of $1,777,456 on parking fees, how much money did it lose on operations other than parking fees?

Name ____

PRACTICE WORKSHEET 27

Permutations and Combinations

1. There are eight running backs on a team. If the coach started two running backs, how many combinations could he choose from?

2. If a team has jerseys in three different styles, helmets in two different styles, and pants in three different styles, how many combinations of uniforms are there to choose from?

3. A team's uniform consists of two colors, but they have five colors to choose from. How many combinations of uniforms do they have?

4. Before a game, eight referees line up in single file for the National Anthem. In how many ways can the referees line up in single file?

Name ______________________________________

PRACTICE WORKSHEET 28

Unit Conversions

1. The length of a football field is 100 yards. What is the length of a field in inches? In centimeters? (2.5 centimeters = 1 inch)

2. A player gained 125 yards rushing. How many feet did he gain?

3. The width of a football field is 160 feet. What is the width of the field in yards?

4. If the length of a football field is 10,800 inches, find its length in millimeters. *Hint:* 10 mm = 1 cm

5. A team spent 4,200 minutes practicing last week. How many hours did they spend practicing?

6. A team is scheduled to play their next game in exactly 3 days, 4 hours. How many hours until they play their next game? How many minutes?

Name ____

PRACTICE WORKSHEET 29

Evaluating Algebraic Expressions

Evaluate $\frac{1}{8}(T) + \frac{1}{24}(V) + \frac{1}{48}(P + R + C) - \frac{1}{12}(I) - \frac{1}{16}(F)$ if

1. $T = 2$
   $V = 1$
   $P = 14$
   $R = 3$
   $C = 0$
   $I = 2$
   $F = 0$

2. $T = 3$
   $V = 0$
   $P = 1$
   $R = 17$
   $C = 7$
   $I = 4$
   $F = 1$

Evaluate $\left(\frac{W}{S}\right) 360$ if:

3. $W = \frac{3}{8}$

   $S = 1\frac{33}{48}$

4. $W = \frac{1}{2}$

   $S = 2\frac{1}{2}$

Name ______________________________

PRACTICE WORKSHEET 30

Properties of Mathematics

Distributive property	$a(b + c) = ab + ac$
Commutative property of addition	$a + b = b + a$
Commutative property of multiplication	$ab = ba$
Associative property of addition	$a + (b + c) = (a + b) + c$
Associative property of multiplication	$a(bc) = (ab)c$
Inverse property of addition	$a + (-a) = 0$
Inverse property of multiplication	$a \times \frac{1}{a} = 1$
Identity property of addition	$a + 0 = a$
Identity property of multiplication	$a(1) = a$

The following equations are used to compute the points earned in various Fantasy sports. List the mathematical property of each, and fill in the missing term.

1. $\frac{7}{48}C + \frac{1}{2}R + \frac{3}{8}P = \frac{1}{2}R + \frac{3}{8}P +$ ________

   Property: ______________________________

2. $\frac{2}{21}R \times \frac{3}{11}C = \frac{3}{11}C \times$ ________

   Property: ______________________________

3. $\frac{3}{5}\left(P + \frac{1}{2}\right) = \frac{3}{5}P +$ ________

   Property: ______________________________

Properties of Mathematics *(Cont'd.)*

4. $\frac{3}{24}R + \left(\frac{1}{4}C + \frac{2}{5}P\right) =$ ________ $\left(\frac{3}{24}R + \text{——}\right) + \frac{2}{5}P$

Property: ____

5. $\frac{1}{5}P \times \left(\frac{3}{10}C \times \frac{2}{9}R\right) =$ ________ $\left(\text{—} \times \frac{3}{10}C\right) \times \frac{2}{9}R$

Property: ____

6. $\frac{9}{48}C + ($________$) = 0$

Property: ____

7. $\frac{5}{12}P(0) =$ ________

Property: ____

8. $2\frac{1}{8} +$ ________ $= 2\frac{1}{8}$

Property: ____

9. ________ $(1) = \frac{31}{48}$

Property: ____

Name ______________________________

PRACTICE WORKSHEET 31

Graphing on a Number Line

(Use with Handout 12)

Example

During the first six weeks, Jesse Wade's range of points earned was between and $\frac{9}{48}$ and $\frac{30}{48}$, inclusive. Using these data, we can graph the range of points earned by Wade on a number line.

$\frac{9}{48}$ •———• $\frac{30}{48}$

Use a number line to graph the range of points earned from weeks 1–6 for the following players.

1. Ty Johnson ______________________________

2. Josh Maris ______________________________

3. Ollie Mays ______________________________

4. D. J. Tucker ______________________________

5. Tao Faumuina ______________________________

6. Tigers ______________________________

Name ________________________________

PRACTICE WORKSHEET 32

Linear Equations (A)

The equations below are used to compute total weekly points or to find the measurement of central angles in a circle graph. In each case, solve for the variable.

1. $\frac{1}{8}(3) + \frac{1}{24}(1) + \frac{1}{48}(P + 5 + 12) - \frac{1}{12}(0) - \frac{1}{16}(2) = \frac{11}{16}$

2. $\frac{1}{8}(4) + \frac{1}{24}(0) + \frac{1}{48}(15 + R + 8) - \frac{1}{12}(2) - \frac{1}{16}(1) = \frac{13}{16}$

3. $\frac{1}{8}(2) + \frac{1}{24}(1) + \frac{1}{48}(0 + 1 + C) - \frac{1}{12}(0) - \frac{1}{16}(2) = \frac{9}{16}$

4. $\frac{1}{8}(T) + \frac{1}{24}(0) + \frac{1}{48}(7 + 3 + 0) - \frac{1}{12}(3) - \frac{1}{16}(2) = \frac{1}{8}$

5. $w \div 4 \times 360 = 180$

Linear Equations (A) *(Cont'd.)*

6. $\frac{w}{3} \times 360 = 40$

7. $\frac{1}{8} \div s \times 360 = 30$

8. $\frac{1}{2} \div 2.5 \times 360 = A$

9. $\frac{w}{2.25} \times 360 = 90$

10. $.6^0(3) + .6^{-1}(0) + .6^{-2}(0 + 4 + C) - .6^{-3}(0) - .6^{-4}(1) = 25.84$

Linear Equations (A) *(Cont'd.)*

11. $2^4(2) + 2^2(V) + 2^3(7 + 1 + 0) - 2^4(2) - 2^5(1) = 8$

12. $4^{-1}(T) + 4^{-2}(0) + 4^{-3}(0 + 8 + 8) - 4^{-4}(0) - 4^{-5}(0) = 1$

13. $\left(\sum_{j=1}^{6} j\right)(1) + \left(\sum_{j=1}^{5} j\right)(0) + \left(\sum_{j=1}^{4} j\right)(2 + R + 2) - \left(\sum_{j=1}^{3} j\right)(0) - \left(\sum_{j=1}^{2} j\right)(1) = 79$

14. $6!(2) + 5!(1) + 4!(0 + 10 + C) - 3!(1) - 2!(2) = 1958$

Linear Equations (A) *(Cont'd.)*

15. $\frac{5}{6}(4) + \frac{4}{5}(0) + \frac{3}{4}(10 + 2 + 2) - \frac{2}{7}(I) - \frac{2}{8}(0) = 13.5476$

16. $\left(\frac{5}{6}\right)^0 (T) + \left(\frac{4}{5}\right)^1 (1) + \left(\frac{3}{4}\right)^2 (8 + 5 + 0) - \left(\frac{2}{7}\right)^3 (0) - \left(\frac{1}{4}\right)^4 (2) = 11.1046875$

17. $-.075\,(2) - .025\,(0) - .0125\,(16 + 2 + 0) + .05\,(0) + .0375\,(F) = -.3$

18. $.06\,(0) + .02\,(0) + .01\,(0 + 0 + 4) - .04\,(I) - .03\,(3) = -.09$

Name ______________________________

PRACTICE WORKSHEET 33

Linear Equations (B)

In the problems below, insert the values shown for each variable in the total points equation. Then solve for W, and write the answer in its simplest form.

$$\frac{1}{8}(T) + \frac{1}{24}(V) + \frac{1}{48}(P + R + C) - \frac{1}{12}(I) - \frac{1}{16}(F) = W$$

1. $P = 3$
   $R = 2$
   $C = 4$
   $T = 3$
   $V = 1$
   $I = 4$
   $F = 2$
   $W =$

2. $P = 7$
   $C = 4$
   $T = 2$
   $R = 5$
   $V = 2$
   $I = 1$
   $F = 3$
   $W =$

3. $R = 3$
   $P = 11$
   $C = 7$
   $V = 0$
   $T = 4$
   $I = 2$
   $F = 2$
   $W =$

Name ____

PRACTICE WORKSHEET 34

Area and Perimeter of Rectangles

1. Explain the meaning of the variables in the following equations:

$$P = 2l + 2w$$

$$A = bh$$

2. The rectangular dimensions of a professional football field are 160 by 360 feet. This includes the end zones, each of which is 30 feet in length. The width and length of a junior field (for younger players) is 100 feet by 180 feet. Find the area and perimeter of both football fields. Then find the ratio of the area of the professional field to the area of the junior field in each measurement unit. Do you see any patterns? Explain your answer.

	Area of Professional Field	Area of Junior Field	Ratio of Area of Professional Field to Area of Junior Field
Square feet			
Square inches			
Square yards			
Square centimeters (2.5 cm. = 1 inch)			
Square millimeters			
Square meters			

3. If artificial turf costs $35 per square foot, how much would it cost to resurface a field, including the end zones?

Area and Perimeter of Rectangles *(Cont'd.)*

4. How much would it cost to resurface the junior field if the price of artificial turf was $20 per square foot?

5. Find the perimeter of a professional football field, a soccer field, a professional basketball court, and a high school basketball court. Then make two statements comparing the areas of any two of the playing surfaces. For example, you may predict that a football field is three times larger than a basketball court, or that a soccer field is 25% larger than a rugby field. Then find the actual area, and see how close your predictions were.

Statement 1:

Statement 2:

Playing Surface	***Dimensions***	***Area***	***Perimeter***
Professional football field	300 ft. by 160 ft.		
Soccer field	68 m by 105 m		
Professional basketball court	94 ft. by 50 ft.		
High school basketball court	84 ft. by 45 ft.		

Name ____

PRACTICE WORKSHEET 35

Golden Rectangles

A Golden Rectangle is a rectangle in which the ratio of its length to its width is about 1.6:1.

1. Fill in the chart below.

	Dimensions	Ratio of Length to Width	Difference from Golden Rectangle Ratio
Professional basketball court	94 ft. by 50 ft.		
Football field	300 ft. by 160 ft.		
College/high school basketball court	84 ft. by 50 ft.		
Soccer field	105 m. by 68 m.		
Junior basketball court	74 ft. by 42 ft.		

2. Which playing surfaces have a ratio that approximates that of a Golden Rectangle?

3. Measure the length and width of various objects to find examples of Golden Rectangles. Some suggestions: flags, calculators, books, blackboards, windows, doors, file cabinets.

4. Predict the ratio of your height to the span of your two arms. Find the ratio. What did you learn?

Name ____

PRACTICE WORKSHEET 36

Functions

In the exercises below, (1) write the function rule and (2) solve for the variable.

1. X = number of touchdowns; Y = points earned.

   Function rule: ____

X	Y
1	$\frac{6}{48}$
2	$\frac{12}{48}$
3	$\frac{18}{48}$
7	*n*

2. X = number of rushing yards in sets of 10; Y = points earned.

   Function rule: ____

X	Y
1	$\frac{1}{48}$
3	$\frac{3}{48}$
5	$\frac{5}{48}$
13	*n*

Functions *(Cont'd.)*

3. X = number of field goals; Y = number of points earned.

   Function rule: ______________________________

X	Y
7	$\frac{7}{16}$
14	$\frac{14}{16}$
21	$\frac{21}{16}$
35	n

4. Construct your own function chart below.

   Function rule: ______________________________

X	Y

Name ______________________________

PRACTICE WORKSHEET 37

Area and Circumference of Circles

Area of circle = πr^2

Circumference of circle = πd

r = radius; d = diameter; $\pi = 3.14$

1. A circular logo located at the center of the football field has a diameter of 38 feet. Find the area and circumference of the logo.

2. If the area of a logo is 100.48 square feet, what is the diameter of the logo?

3. If a circular logo has a diameter of 15 feet, what is the area of the logo?

4. On a basketball court, the circle at the center of the court has a radius of 4 feet. Find the diameter, circumference, and area of the circle.

   Diameter: ______________________________

   Circumference: ______________________________

   Area: ______________________________

5. If the circumference of a logo on a shirt is 5 inches, what are the radius, diameter, and area of the logo?

   Radius: ______________________________

   Diameter: ______________________________

   Area: ______________________________

Name ____________________

PRACTICE WORKSHEET 38

Weight

Predict and then find the weight of the following objects, in the given units. You will need a scale.

	Predicted Weight			Actual Weight		
	Pounds	**Ounces**	**Grams**	**Pounds**	**Ounces**	**Grams**
Football						
Basketball						
Baseball						
Soccer ball						
Table tennis ball						
Hockey puck						

For each of the following problems, predict the answer, then solve the problem.

1. How many table tennis balls would weigh as much as a football? As much as a tennis ball? As much as a hockey puck?

2. Which is greater: the weight of 3 hockey pucks or 7 basketballs?

3. Which is less: the weight of 1,000 table tennis balls or 10 footballs?

4. How many table tennis balls would it take to equal your body weight? How many soccer balls?

Name ____

PRACTICE WORKSHEET 39

Pythagorean Theorem

In a right triangle,

$$a^2 + b^2 = c^2$$

where

a = length of one leg of the triangle
b = length of the other leg of the triangle
c = length of the hypotenuse

Use the Pythagorean Theorem to solve the following problems:

1. The distance between consecutive bases on a baseball diamond is 30 yards. Find the distance from first base to third base.

2. Find the length of the diagonal of a football field if the length is 300 feet and the width is 160 feet.

3. Find the length of the diagonal of a basketball court if the length is 94 feet and the width is 50 feet.

4. Find the width of a soccer field if the length is 105 meters and the length of the diagonal is 125 meters.

5. Find the width of a lacrosse field if the length of the field is 112 yards and the length of the diagonal is 133 yards.

Name ______________________________

PRACTICE WORKSHEET 40

Mean, Median, Mode, and Range

(Use with Handout 12)

1. For each of the first six weeks, find the points earned by each player on the Wildcats. In the table below, record the mean, median, mode, and range for the points earned for each of the first six weeks.

Week	Mean	Median	Mode	Range
1				
2				
3				
4				
5				
6				

2. For each of the first six weeks, find the points earned by each player on your team. In the table below, record the mean, median, mode, and range of the points earned for each of the first six weeks.

Week	Mean	Median	Mode	Range
1				
2				
3				
4				
5				
6				

Name ______________________________

PRACTICE WORKSHEET 41

Probability

1. Last year, a quarterback threw 25% of his passes to the left side of the field, 35% to the right side, and 40% straight downfield. If the quarterback attempted 600 passes last year, how many passes did he throw in each direction?

2. Using only the data in problem 1, what is the probability that the quarterback's first pass this year will be to his left side?

3. A team's record during the past 10 years is 90–70. Without taking any other variables into account, what should the team's record be this year?

4. In how many ways can you express the outcome if the probability that an event will occur is 25%? *Hint:* $\frac{1}{4}$.

5. If the probability that an event will occur is 55%, what is the probability that the event will not occur?

Probability *(Cont'd.)*

6. The letters in "Gar Jendvat" are placed into a hat. Find the probability of the following random events.

   A. Selecting the letter *v*

   B. Selecting the letters *d, e,* or *r*

   C. Selecting the letter *z*

   D. Selecting any letter except *r*

   E. Selecting the letter *g,* replacing it, then selecting the letter *g* again

   F. Selecting the letters *d* and *j* on consecutive draws (without replacing letters)

In exercises 7–11, you are given $P(Q)$, the probability that a player will rush for 100 yards in a given game. Find $P(\text{not } Q)$, the probability that event Q will not occur.

7. $P(Q) = \frac{27}{48}$ $\quad P(\text{not } Q) =$

8. $P(Q) = .435$ $\quad P(\text{not } Q) =$

9. $P(Q) = 39\%$ $\quad P(\text{not } Q) =$

10. $P(Q) = 1$ $\quad P(\text{not } Q) =$

11. $P(Q) = 0$ $\quad P(\text{not } Q) =$

Name ____

PRACTICE WORKSHEET 42

Circle Graphs

(Use with Handout 12)

$W \div S \times 360 = A$

W = total weekly points for one player
S = total weekly points for the team
A = the measurement of the central angle of the circle graph

Example

In week 4, Jesse Wade earned $\frac{14}{48}$ points. Find the measurement of the central angle representing Wade's portion of his team's total points for that week.

$$\frac{14}{48} \div \frac{43}{48} \times 360 = 117.2^\circ$$

1. Find the measurement of the central angles for all players on the Wildcats for week 4.

2. Find the measurement of the central angles for all players on the Wildcats for week 5.

3. Find the measurement of the central angles showing the cumulative points for the players on the Wildcats for weeks 1–6.

4. If the central angle in a circle graph is 30 degrees, what percentage of the graph will that section represent?

5. If the central angle in a circle graph is 45 degrees, what percentage of the graph will that section represent?

6. If one section of a circle graph represented 75% of the total graph, what is the measurement of the corresponding central angle?

7. The sum of the percentages inside a circle graph is 359 degrees. Explain how this could occur.

Name ____

PRACTICE WORKSHEET 43

Stem-and-Leaf Plots and Histograms

1. The following values represent the weekly point totals (in 48ths) for the Wildcats for a 16-game season. Using graph paper, construct a stem-and-leaf plot and histogram.

66	79	38	50	106	66	69	111
121	88	85	77	70	49	100	95

2. The following values represent the weekly point totals (in 48ths) for Ollie Mays for a 16-game season. Using graph paper, construct a stem-and-leaf plot and histogram based on the data below.

23	9	17	21	12	10	8	31
41	26	34	29	4	10	16	37

Name ____

PRACTICE WORKSHEET 44

Scatter Plots

1. The table below represents hypothetical ticket prices from 1990 to 1999. On graph paper, construct a scatter plot of these data. Does the scatter plot have a positive or negative correlation? Explain your answer.

Year	Average Price per Ticket
1990	$32.65
1991	$34.87
1992	$38.57
1993	$40.25
1994	$42.56
1995	$45.79
1996	$47.03
1997	$51.11
1998	$53.66
1999	$55.74

2. The table below shows the weight and maximum bench presses of several football players. Using graph paper, construct a scatter plot for these data. Does the scatter plot have a positive or negative correlation? Explain your answer.

Player	Weight of Player	Maximum Bench Press
A	225	320
B	190	250
C	345	450
D	330	425
E	255	410
F	255	430
G	340	480
H	330	490
I	185	260

Name ____

PRACTICE WORKSHEET 45

Box-and-Whisker Plots

The following data sets represent the weekly points earned (in 48ths) by Josh Maris and the total weekly team points earned by the Wildcats for the first twelve weeks of the season. Using graph paper, draw a box-and-whisker plot for each set of data. Label the medians as well as the upper and lower quartiles.

1. Josh Maris 23, 9, 17, 21, 12, 10, 8, 31, 37, 42, 35, 18

2. English Wildcats 66, 79, 38, 50, 106, 66, 69, 111, 49, 100, 95, 81

Name ____

PRACTICE WORKSHEET 46

Statements Using Math Terminology

Statements are complete sentences based on a set of data, and they must be accompanied by mathematical proof. The following statements were derived from week 1 on Handout 12.

Example

Ty Johnson earned one-fifth as many points as Jessie Wade earned.

$$\frac{1}{5} \times \frac{30}{48} = \frac{6}{48}$$

For the following statements, show the mathematical proof.

1. The wide receivers earned more points than the running backs did.

2. Jesse Wade and Ollie Mays accounted for over 63% of the total points earned by the Wildcats.

3. Angel Ramos earned approximately 8% of his team's total points.

4. D. J. Tucker earned twice as many points as the Tigers defense earned.

5. Josh Maris and Ty Johnson earned one-half as many points as D. J. Tucker earned.

6. Ollie Mays earned 27.4% of his team's total points.

7. Use Handout 12 to write five statements, and show the mathematical proof for each.
   1.
   2.
   3.
   4.
   5.

Name ____

EXTRA CREDIT WORKSHEET

Extra Credit Problems

1. Each time a basketball bounces, it rebounds to 75% of its height on the previous rebound. The ball was originally dropped from the top of a building that has a height of 150 feet. Construct a table of the number of bounces and the rebound height of each bounce. On which bounce does the ball bounce less than 1 foot high?

2. Find the stadium seating capacity, average ticket price, and revenue for two professional football teams. In this case, revenue is defined as the number of tickets sold, multiplied by the average price of a ticket, multiplied by 8, which is the number of regular-season home games each team plays during one season.

   A. What is the difference in revenue between the two teams for one game? For one season?

   B. How much would revenue increase for one game for both teams if they increased ticket prices by an average of 5%?

   C. How much would revenue decrease for the season for both teams if they decreased ticket prices by an average of 3%?

3. Predict how many small (8-inch diameter), medium (12-inch diameter), or large (16-inch diameter) pizzas would fit on a football field. Then find the actual number of pizzas.

Chapter Five

Quizzes

The quizzes in this chapter can be used to analyze student progress and provide timely feedback in order to improve student achievement. They also provide students with multiple exposures to content.

Research indicates that learning is maximized when assessment closely monitors the learning objectives. Consequently, the quizzes in this chapter are aligned with the corresponding worksheets. They can be used to assess student progress or they can be used as additional worksheets.

Research also indicates that learning is facilitated when visual materials are included in the learning environment. The inclusion of visual materials (in the form of charts, diagrams, or other data depiction) lessens the cognitive load on students. This is particularly true for special needs students. In order to take advantage of this research, several quizzes have been designed to be used in conjunction with Handout 12, a stacked-bar graph.

Some quizzes may be time-consuming, depending on the skill level of students (for example, the quizzes in which students construct graphs).

Name ___

QUIZ 1

Rounding Whole Numbers and Expanded Notation

1. Round the following player salaries to the nearest 10,000, 100,000, and 1,000,000.

Salary	***Nearest $10,000***	***Nearest $100,000***	***Nearest $1,000,000***
$4,822,885			
$7,343,992			
$3,335,005			
$2,445,008			

2. Use expanded notation to represent the following player salaries:
   $3,556,877

   $6,902,889

   $9,999,009

   $ 755,555

3. Write the following in standard notation:
   20,000,000 + 2,000,000 + 600,000 + 4,000 + 700 + 20 + 9 = ___

   4,000,000 + 900,000 + 30,000 + 600 + 80 + 5 = ___

   10,000,000 + 2,000,000 + 500,000 + 60,000 + 8,000 + 600 + 70 + 2 = ___

Name ____

QUIZ 2

Least Common Multiple and Greatest Common Factor

The points scored by a team during one season are listed below. Find the least common multiple and greatest common factor for each pair of numbers.

Weeks	***Points Scored***	***Least Common Multiple***	***Greatest Common Factor***
Weeks 1, 2	12, 36		
Weeks 3, 4	18, 27		
Weeks 5, 6	33, 9		
Weeks 7, 8	21, 42		
Weeks 9, 10	15, 6		

Name ______________________________

QUIZ 3

Operations with Whole Numbers

1. What is the difference between the most expensive and least expensive players listed below?

Player A	$15,000,886
Player B	$14,950,351
Player C	$14,800,995
Player D	$14,675,228
Player E	$14,650,774
Player F	$14,425,005
Player G	$ 1,320,555

2. A player's salary is $25,000,000. He spent $16,007,536. How much money does he have left to spend?

3. What is the average cost of the players in problem 1?

4. If a player rushes for 1,555 yards in 10 games, what is his rushing average per game?

5. If 12 players on a team each have a salary of $500,500, what is the sum of their salaries?

Name ____________________

QUIZ 4

Equivalent Fractions

List the first three equivalent fractions for each player's points.

1. Jesse Wade $\frac{5}{8}$ ______ ______ ______

2. Ty Johnson $\frac{5}{16}$ ______ ______ ______

3. Josh Maris $\frac{12}{48}$ ______ ______ ______

4. Ollie Mays $\frac{1}{24}$ ______ ______ ______

5. E.D.J. Tucker $\frac{1}{4}$ ______ ______ ______

6. Tao Faumuina $\frac{13}{48}$ ______ ______ ______

7. Angel Ramos $\frac{1}{6}$ ______ ______ ______

8. Tigers $\frac{1}{8}$ ______ ______ ______

Name ____

QUIZ 5

Patterns and Multiples

(Use with Handout 12)

1. Find the first three multiples for the points Ollie Mays earned for week 2.

2. Find the first three multiples for the points Josh Maris earned for week 3.

3. Find the first three multiples for the points Ty Johnson earned for week 1.

4. If $\frac{30}{48}$ is the third multiple of a number, what is the original number?

5. If 4.5 is the fourth multiple of a number, what is the original number?

Name ____

QUIZ 6

Ordering Fractions and Decimals

1. Use inequalities to arrange the following fractions in ascending order.

Chad Small	$\frac{33}{48}$
Rudi Price	$\frac{1}{3}$
Tar Bruckman	$\frac{12}{48}$
Tony Biggs	$\frac{8}{24}$
Larue Bennett	$\frac{1}{2}$
Brandon Wietz	$\frac{1}{8}$
John Stevens	$\frac{1}{4}$
Tigers	$\frac{3}{16}$

2. Use inequalities to arrange the following decimals in descending order.

Jess Horry	.33
Tom Vorency	.5
Philip Vons	.125
Oliver Masten	.5625
Randy Utley	.625
Lloyd Benson	.375
Derrick Hanson	.25
Tigers	.125

Name ____

QUIZ 7

Rounding Decimals

(Use with Handout 12)

1. Round the cumulative points for the following players on the Wildcats for weeks 1–3 to the nearest tenth, hundredth, and thousandth.

	Johnson	Maris	Mays	Tucker	Faumuina	Ramos	Tigers
Total Points in Weeks 1–3 (Fraction)							
Total Points in Weeks 1–3 (Decimal)							
Nearest Tenth							
Nearest Hundredth							
Nearest Thousandth							

2. Use the table below to round the cumulative points for your players for weeks 1–6.

Player	QB	RB	RB	WR	WR	K	Defense
Total Points in Weeks 1–3 (Fraction)							
Total Points in Weeks 1–3 (Decimal)							
Nearest Tenth							
Nearest Hundredth							
Nearest Thousandth							

Name ______________________________

QUIZ 8

Improper Fractions, Mixed Numbers, and Reciprocals

Convert the following points to mixed numbers, and write each in its simplest form.

1. $\frac{84}{48}$

2. $\frac{42}{48}$

3. $\frac{53}{48}$

4. $\frac{111}{48}$

5. $\frac{76}{48}$

6. $\frac{90}{48}$

7. $\frac{120}{48}$

Write the reciprocals (in their simplest form) for the original fractions given in items 1–7.

8.

9.

10.

11.

12.

13.

14.

Name ______________________________

QUIZ 9

Adding and Subtracting Fractions

(Use with Handout 12)

1. For week 3, find the sum of the points earned by Jesse Wade, Ollie Mays, and Angel Ramos.

2. For week 5, find the sum of the points earned by the Wildcats, with the exception of Josh Maris and D. J. Tucker.

3. For week 6, find the sum of the points earned by Ollie Mays, D. J. Tucker, and Tao Faumuina.

4. For week 4, how many more points did Ty Johnson and Josh Maris earn compared to Ollie Mays, D. J. Tucker, and Tao Faumuina?

5. For week 2, find the sum of the points earned by all players, with the exception of Jesse Wade and Ollie Mays.

Name ____

QUIZ 10

Stacked-Bar Graphs

Using graph paper and an interval of $\frac{4}{48}$, construct a stacked-bar graph based on the data below.

Player	***Week 1***	***Week 2***	***Week 3***
David Barstow	$\frac{3}{8}$	$\frac{5}{12}$	$\frac{1}{6}$
Kevan Jossy	$\frac{1}{3}$	$\frac{19}{48}$	$\frac{1}{6}$
Sammy McAllister	$\frac{1}{8}$	$\frac{5}{24}$	$\frac{1}{4}$

Name ____

QUIZ 11

Multiplying and Dividing Fractions

(Use with Handout 12)

1. How many weeks would it take a player to earn $4\frac{12}{48}$ points if he averaged $\frac{6}{8}$ points a week?

2. What is the product of the points earned by Jesse Wade and the Tigers defense during week 6?

3. The product of the points that Tyrue Campbell and Jeremy Grattis earned during the season was $1\frac{7}{8}$. If Campbell earned $1\frac{1}{2}$ points, how many points did Grattis earn?

4. A player earned $6\frac{1}{6}$ points during the 16-game season. How many points did he average per week?

5. If Brian Tollson earned $4\frac{1}{4}$ points for the season and Hank Johnson earned $1\frac{21}{48}$ points for 1 week, how many weeks would it take Johnson to match Tollson?

Name ____

QUIZ 12

Rounding Fractions

(Use with Handout 12)

1. In the table below, round each player's cumulative points from weeks 3–6 to the nearest $\frac{1}{2}$, $\frac{1}{4}$, and $\frac{1}{8}$.

	Wade	**Mays**	**Tucker**	**Maris**	**Tigers**
Nearest $\frac{1}{2}$					
Nearest $\frac{1}{4}$					
Nearest $\frac{1}{8}$					

2. In the table below, round each player's cumulative points from weeks 1–3 to the nearest $\frac{1}{2}$, $\frac{1}{4}$, and $\frac{1}{8}$.

	Wade	**Mays**	**Tucker**	**Maris**	**Tigers**
Nearest $\frac{1}{2}$					
Nearest $\frac{1}{4}$					
Nearest $\frac{1}{8}$					

Name ____

QUIZ 13

Multiplying and Dividing Decimals

1. During the past 5 years, a quarterback posted ratings of 98.64, 101.88, 76.75, 90.09, and 94.53. Find his average rating for the past 5 years.

2. If a football player worked 8 hours a day, 175 days a year, and his salary was $5.4 million for 1 year, how much money did he make each working day? Each working hour? Each working minute? Each working second? Round your answers to the nearest cent.

3. If a snail can crawl at a rate of .09 yards per minute, how many minutes will it take the snail to crawl the length of a football field (100 yards)?

4. If 50,000 fans each consumed an average of 7.75 ounces of soda at a game, what is the total amount of soda consumed at the game?

5. A vendor selling ice cream sandwiches earns $6.75 an hour, plus 45 cents for each sandwich sold. Find the income for the vendor if she worked 4 hours and sold 340 ice cream sandwiches.

Name ____

QUIZ 14

Unit Rates

1. At a game, you can purchase 12 ounces of peanuts for $3.75 or 20 ounces for $4.75. What is the lower price per ounce?

2. If Rachel Jolson drove her car 300 miles on 20 gallons of gas and Keneesha Slammer drove her car 450 miles on 15 gallons of gas, how many miles per gallon did each car get?

3. If Danielle Bonte can purchase 100 acres for $2.5 million or 75 acres for $1.5 million, what is the lower price per acre?

4. If fans can purchase a 10-game season ticket for $650 or a 1-game ticket for $75, what is the lower price per game?

5. How much less per year is a salary of $4.5 million for 10 years compared to a salary of $8.5 million for 15 years?

Name ____

QUIZ 15

Converting Fractions, Decimals, and Percentages

1. Convert the points below to decimals. Then round to the nearest thousandth.

Player	***Points***	***Decimal***	***Rounded to Nearest Thousandth***
A. Jimmy Brooks	$\frac{20}{48}$	______	______
B. Jon Lewis	$\frac{2}{3}$	______	______
C. Alfred James	$\frac{12}{48}$	______	______
D. Reggie Gluckman	$\frac{7}{24}$	______	______
E. Eric Santos	$\frac{1}{2}$	______	______
F. Marty Mason	$\frac{5}{8}$	______	______
G. Jason Klodestes	$\frac{1}{4}$	______	______
H. Tigers	$\frac{5}{16}$	______	______

2. Convert the following points earned to fractions and percentages.

Player	***Points***	***Fraction***	***Percentage***
A. Tad Duce	.825	______	______
B. Buddy Crisp	.5625	______	______
C. Ellis Horn	.125	______	______
D. Jole Gupp	.5	______	______
E. Pete Marrick	.3333	______	______
F. Paul Yultman	.375	______	______
G. Jeff Notel	.25	______	______

Name ____

QUIZ 16

Ratios

1. If it took a player three weeks to earn $\frac{12}{16}$ points, how many weeks would it take him to earn $4\frac{1}{4}$ points?

2. If it took Guy Staley 12 weeks to earn $12\frac{12}{48}$ points, how many weeks would it take him to earn 10 points?

3. A player earned $16\frac{16}{48}$ points for the entire season. If he earned an equal number of points each week in a 16-game season, how many points would he have accumulated after 9 weeks?

4. If a player earned $\frac{3}{48}$ points the first week, how many points is he projected to earn in a 16-game season?

5. During week 12, the ratio of Roddy Shells's points to Daniel Harrison's points was 1:3. If Harrison earned $\frac{15}{48}$ points, how many points did Shells earn?

Name____

QUIZ 17

Percentage of Price Increase and Decrease

1. If the price of an autographed football rose from $125 to $325 during the past year, what is the percentage of price increase?

2. If the price of a season ticket decreased from $875 to $800, what is the percentage of price decrease?

3. If the price of a season ticket increased from $700 to $770, what is the percentage of price increase?

4. If a player's salary increased from $25 million to $26.5 million, what is the percentage increase?

5. If the salary cap for a team rose to $75 million from $72 million, what is the percentage increase?

Name ____

QUIZ 18

Finding a Percentage of a Number

1. What percentage of LaShawn Tomlin's points did Adam Dunlevay earn?

$$\text{Tomlin } \frac{36}{48}$$

$$\text{Dunlevay } \frac{3}{16}$$

2. Rod Derringer earned $\frac{20}{48}$ points, which was 40% of Ralph Robinson's points. How many points did Robinson earn?

3. During week 9, a player earned 250% of his week 8 point total of $(\frac{6}{48})$. How many points did he earn?

4. During Week 9, a player earned 150% of his week 8 point total $(\frac{18}{48})$. How many points did he earn?

5. During week 16, Thomas Arraya earned $\frac{12}{48}$ points, which was 300% of Chad Jordan's points for that week. How many points did Jordan earn that week?

Name ____

QUIZ 19

Proportions

1. If a player earned $2\frac{5}{16}$ points during the first 6 weeks of the season, how many points is he projected to earn for a 16-game season?

2. If Clint Jackson took 4 weeks to earn $\frac{1}{2}$ points, how many weeks would it take him to earn $1\frac{24}{48}$ points?

3. If a player took 12 weeks to earn $2\frac{1}{48}$ points, how many weeks would it take him to earn $8\frac{1}{12}$ points?

4. Bruno Collins earned 4 points for a 16-game season. If he earned an equal number of points each week, how many points would he have accumulated after 9 weeks?

5. Rudi Brown earned 3 points for a 16-game season. If he earned an equal number of points each week, how many points would he have accumulated after 7 weeks?

Name ____

QUIZ 20

Ratios and Proportions

1. During week 9, the ratio of Lake Foster's points to Monte Brown's points was 3:4. If Brown earned $\frac{12}{48}$ points that week, how many points did Foster earn?

2. During week 10, the ratio of Tatum Rottey's points to Gary Porter's points was 3:1. If Porter earned $\frac{24}{48}$ points that week, how many points did Rottey earn?

3. During week 11, the ratio of Will Palmer's points to Oliver Jackson's points was 2:5. If Palmer earned $\frac{30}{48}$ points that week, how many points did Jackson earn?

4. During week 13, the ratio of Larry Nice's points to Morten McKay's points was 2:3. If McKay earned $\frac{27}{48}$ points that week, how many points did Nice earn?

5. During week 9, the ratio of David Leads's points to Hal Suggs's points was 21:7. If Suggs earned $\frac{7}{8}$ points that week, how many points did Leads earn?

Name ____

QUIZ 21

Factoring

1. A player earned $\frac{28}{48}$ points during week 16. If one factor of $\frac{28}{48}$ is $\frac{7}{12}$, what is the other factor?

2. What is the smallest product for the points earned by any two players in the following list?

Jesse Wade	$\frac{39}{48}$
Ty Johnson	$\frac{4}{16}$
Josh Maris	$\frac{2}{24}$
Ollie Mays	$\frac{19}{48}$
D. J. Tucker	$\frac{5}{16}$
Tao Faumuina	$\frac{16}{48}$
Angel Ramos	$\frac{3}{8}$

3. What is the product of the points earned by Johnson and Faumuina?

4. What is the product of the points earned by Johnson and Ramos?

Name ____

QUIZ 22

Interest, Depreciation, and Tax

A player signed a 10-year contract for $95,000,000. Answer the following questions, based on the assumption that his income remains constant during the life of the contract.

1. If the player invests 65% of his annual salary for 3 years at a rate of 7% for each year, how much interest will he earn each year if the interest is compounded annually? Construct a spreadsheet showing the interest earned and the total value of his account at the end of each year. Use the following formula:

   I = PRT
   I = interest earned
   P = principle
   R = interest rate
   T = time

2. If the player purchases a sports car for $380,000 and the state sales tax rate is 8.5%, how much tax will he owe? What will be the total cost of the car?

3. If the value of the car depreciates by 10% each year, what will the car be worth at the end of 3 years? Construct a spreadsheet showing the amount of depreciation and the corresponding value of the car each year.

4. If a player purchased a house for $8,500,000 and the price of the home appreciates 10% a year for the next 2 years, what will be the value of the home at the end of that period? Construct a spreadsheet showing the annual appreciation and the corresponding value of the house at the end of each year.

Name ____

QUIZ 23

Prime Factorization

Weekly point totals (in 48ths) for a team are listed below. Write the prime factorization of each number using exponential notation.

Week	***Point Totals***
Week 1	55
Week 2	72
Week 3	49
Week 4	150
Week 5	63
Week 6	3
Week 7	42
Week 8	51

List the first five prime numbers: ____ ____ ____ ____ ____

Name ______________________________

QUIZ 24

Scientific Notation

The dimensions of a football field are 360 feet by 160 feet. Write the area of the field in scientific notation for the following units of measurement.

1. Square feet ______
2. Square inches ______
3. Square yards ______
4. Square centimeters ______
5. Square millimeters ______
6. Square meters ______

Write the following in scientific notation.

7. 1116.75

8. $\frac{48}{42}$

9. .00075

10. $500\frac{1}{4}$

Write the following in standard form.

11. 6.004×10^{-3}

12. $4{,}381{,}111 \times 10^{7}$

Name ____________________

QUIZ 25

Ordering Integers, Fractions, and Decimals

(Use with Handout 12)

1. The following integers represent temperatures in December for several cities that host football teams. Place them in ascending order on the number line below.

   −23   3   21   −17   −9   −32   21   76   44   −1   −11

   ____

2. The following integers represent rushing yards gained or lost by a quarterback during the first 10 games of the season. Place them in ascending order on the number line below.

   24   −12   7   −21   −55   53   −3   −41   41   2

   ____

3. On the number line below, use fractions to identify the points earned by Wildcats players for week 5.

   ____

4. Place the following numerical values on the number line in ascending order.

   .998 $7\frac{1}{6}$ $-13\frac{1}{3}$ −2.8   −15.004   −1.2

   ____

5. On the number line below, use decimals to identify the points earned in ascending order by Wildcats players for week 4.

   ____

Name ____

QUIZ 26

Operations with Integers

1. If a team was penalized for 15,950 yards over the course of 11 16-game seasons, how many yards did it average in penalties per season? Per game? Round your answers to the nearest whole number.

2. The rushing totals for 10 running backs are listed below. How many total yards did they gain or lose?

   −65 −24 −3 19 −17 −22 −41 −5 −33 21

3. If a player rushed for −11 yards in the first game of the season, how many yards is he projected to lose for a complete 16-game season?

4. If a player gained 112 yards in the first game of the season, how many yards is he projected to gain for the first 8 games?

5. The numbers below represent profit or loss from 4 teams for 1 year. What is the average profit or loss?

   $445,000 $3,722,256 $66,773 −$25,776,232

Name ____

QUIZ 27

Permutations and Combinations

1. There are seven wide receivers on a team. If the coach started three wide receivers, how many combinations can he choose from?

2. If a team has jerseys in five different styles, helmets in three different styles, and pants in three different styles, how many combinations of uniforms are there to choose from?

3. A team's uniform consists of two colors, but there are seven colors to choose from. How many combinations of uniforms are there to choose from?

4. Before a game, seven referees line up in single file for the National Anthem. In how many ways can the referees line up in single file?

Name ____

QUIZ 28

Unit Conversions

1. The width of a football field is 40 yards. What is the width of a football field in inches? In centimeters? *Hint:* 2.5 centimeters = 1 inch.

2. If a player gained 95 yards rushing, how many feet did he gain?

3. If the length of a football field is 300 feet, what is the length in miles?

4. If the length of a football field is 10,800 inches, what is the length in centimeters?

5. A team spent 3,600 minutes practicing last week. How many hours did they spend practicing?

6. A team is scheduled to play its next game in 4 days, 5 hours. How many hours until they play the game? How many minutes?

Name ____

QUIZ 29

Evaluating Algebraic Expressions

Evaluate $\frac{1}{8}(T) + \frac{1}{24}(V) + \frac{1}{48}(P + R + C) - \frac{1}{12}(I) - \frac{1}{16}(F)$ if:

1. $T = 4$
   $V = 1$
   $P = 5$
   $R = 13$
   $C = 2$
   $I = 2$
   $F = 1$

2. $T = 2$
   $V = 0$
   $P = 1$
   $R = 7$
   $C = 3$
   $I = 3$
   $F = 0$

3. $T = 3$
   $V = 2$
   $P = 0$
   $R = 16$
   $C = 4$
   $I = 0$
   $F = 2$

Evaluate $\left(\frac{W}{S}\right) 360$ if:

4. $S = 2\frac{1}{8}$

   $W = \frac{1}{2}$

5. $W = \frac{5}{8}$

   $S = 3\frac{1}{16}$

Name ____

QUIZ 30

Properties of Mathematics

Write one example for each of the properties listed.

Distributive property

Associative property of addition

Identity property of multiplication

Inverse property of addition

Commutative property of multiplication

The following equations are used to compute the points earned in various fantasy sports. List the property of each, and fill in the missing term.

1. $\frac{2}{16}\left(P + \frac{27}{48}\right) = \frac{2}{16}P + \_\_\_\_\_\_$

   Property: ____

2. $\frac{9}{48}C + \frac{1}{2}R + \frac{5}{8}P = \frac{1}{2}R + \frac{5}{8}P + \_\_\_\_\_\_$

   Property: ____

3. $\frac{17}{48}R \times \frac{3}{11}C = \frac{3}{11}C \times \_\_\_\_\_\_$

   Property: ____

4. $\frac{11}{17}P + \_\_\_\_\_\_ = 0$

   Property: ____

5. $\frac{2}{3}P \times \left(\frac{3}{10}C \times \frac{2}{9}R\right) = \left(\_\_\_\_\_\_ \times \frac{3}{10}C\right) \times \frac{2}{9}R$

   Property: ____

Name ____

QUIZ 31

Graphing on a Number Line

(Use with Handout 12)

Use number lines to graph the range of points earned for weeks 2–5 for the following players.

Jesse Wade ______________________________

Ty Johnson ______________________________

Josh Maris ______________________________

Ollie Mays ______________________________

Angel Ramos ______________________________

Name ____

QUIZ 32

Linear Equations (A)

The equations below are used to compute total weekly points or to find the measurement of central angles inside a circle graph. In each case, solve for the variable.

1. $\frac{1}{8}(T) + \frac{1}{24}(1) + \frac{1}{48}(2 + 5 + 12) - \frac{1}{12}(0) - \frac{1}{16}(2) = \frac{11}{16}$

2. $-.075\ (2) - .025\ (0) - .0125\ (P + 3 + 0) + .05\ (0) + .0375(2) = -.3$

3. $\frac{1}{8}(2) + \frac{1}{24}(V) + \frac{1}{48}(16 + 3 + 0) - \frac{1}{12}(0) - \frac{1}{16}(2) = \frac{9}{16}$

4. $\frac{1}{8}(2) + \frac{1}{24}(1) + \frac{1}{48}(0 + R + 0) - \frac{1}{12}(3) - \frac{1}{16}(2) = \frac{1}{8}$

Linear Equations (A) *(Cont'd.)*

5. $\left(W \div 3\frac{1}{2}\right) \times 360 = 720$

6. $\left(W \div 2\frac{1}{8}\right) \times 360 = 40$

7. $\left(\frac{1}{8} \div S\right) \times 360 = 22.5$

8. $\frac{3}{4} \div \frac{3}{8} \times 360 = A$

Name ____________________

QUIZ 33

Linear Equations (B)

In the problems below, insert the variables into the total points equation. Then solve for *W*, and write each answer in its simplest form.

$$\frac{1}{8}(T) + \frac{1}{24}(V) + \frac{1}{48}(P + R + C) - \frac{1}{12}(I) - \frac{1}{16}(F) = W$$

1. $P = 0$
   $R = 5$
   $C = 7$
   $T = 2$
   $V = 2$
   $I = 2$
   $F = 3$
   $W =$

2. $P = 11$
   $C = 6$
   $T = 3$
   $R = 4$
   $V = 0$
   $I = 1$
   $F = 1$
   $W =$

3. $R = 2$
   $P = 3$
   $C = 4$
   $V = 1$
   $T = 5$
   $I = 2$
   $F = 2$
   $W =$

Name ____

QUIZ 34

Area and Perimeter of Rectangles

1. The rectangular dimensions of a football field are 160 feet by 360 feet. Find the area of the field for the following units of measurement.

   Square yards ______

   Square inches ______

   Square centimeters (*Hint:* 2.5 cm = 1 inch) ______

2. If artificial turf costs $45 per square foot, then how much would it cost to resurface the field?

3. Fill in the missing information for rectangles.

Length	Width	Perimeter	Area
15	4		
12			36
	7		35
5		26	
7.5			52.5
	10.5	41	
	150	625	

4. Can a square and rectangle with the same area have different perimeters? If so, show the proof.

5. Can a square and rectangle with the same perimeter have different areas? If so, show the proof.

Name ____________________

QUIZ 35

Golden Rectangles

The ratio of length to width in a golden rectangle is approximately 1.6:1. Fill in the chart below.

	Dimensions	Ratio of Length to Width	Difference from Golden Rectangle Ratio
Football field	120 yds. by 53 yds.		
Soccer field	105 meters by 68 meters		
Professional basketball court	1128 in. by 600 in.		
College/high school basketball court	28 yds. by 17 yds.		
Junior basketball court	25 yds. by 14 yds.		

1. Which of the above playing surfaces have a ratio that approximates that of a Golden Rectangle?

2. What is the ratio of the length to the width of your math textbook? Does the ratio approximate that of a Golden Rectangle?

3. Measure the length and width of the following objects in your classroom, and calculate the difference between their ratios and the ratio of a Golden Rectangle.

Object	***Ratio***	***Difference from Golden Rectangle***
Calculator		
Window		
Door		
Top of desk		
Computer screen		

Name ____

QUIZ 36

Functions

In the exercises below, (1) write the function rule and (2) solve for the variable.

1. X = number of touchdowns; Y = points earned

Function rule: ____

X	*Y*
1	$\frac{3}{48}$
2	$\frac{6}{48}$
3	$\frac{9}{48}$
7	*n*

2. X = number of rushing yards in sets of 10; Y = points earned

Function rule: ____

X	*Y*
1	$\frac{15}{48}$
3	$\frac{45}{48}$
5	$\frac{75}{48}$
13	*n*

Functions *(Cont'd.)*

3. X = number field goals; Y = number of points earned

   Function rule: ______________________________

X	Y
2	$\frac{2}{16}$
4	$\frac{4}{16}$
6	$\frac{6}{16}$
12	n

4. Construct your own function chart below.

   Function rule: ______________________________

X	Y

Name ______________________________

QUIZ 37

Area and Circumference of Circles

1. A circular logo located at the center of the football field has a diameter of 36 feet. Find the area and circumference of the logo. Round your answer to the nearest whole number.

2. If the area of a logo is 100.48 square feet, what is its radius?

3. The logo on a junior football field has a circumference of 25.12 feet. What is the area of the logo?

4. The circle at the center of a basketball court has a radius of 5 feet. Find the diameter, circumference, and area of the circle.

   Diameter: ______________________________

   Circumference: ______________________________

   Area: ______________________________

5. If the circumference of a logo on a shirt is 9.42 inches, what are the radius, diameter, and area of the logo?

   Radius: ______________________________

   Diameter: ______________________________

   Area: ______________________________

Name ____

QUIZ 38

Weight

Predict, and then find, the weight of the following objects in the units specified. You will need a scale.

	Predicted Weight			Actual Weight		
	Pounds	**Ounces**	**Grams**	**Pounds**	**Ounces**	**Grams**
Math textbook						
Pencil						
Calculator						
Baseball bat						

Predict, and then solve, the following.

1. How many pencils would it take to weigh as much as a math textbook? As much as a calculator?

2. Which is greater: the weight of 3 calculators or 70 pencils?

3. Which is less: the weight of 1,000 calculators or 100 baseball bats?

4. How many pencils would it take to equal your body weight?

Name ____

QUIZ 39

Pythagorean Theorem

Use the Pythagorean Theorem to solve the following problems.

1. The distance between consecutive bases on a baseball diamond is 90 feet. Find the distance from home plate to second base.

2. Find the length of the diagonal of a football field if the length is 360 feet and the width is 160 feet.

3. Find the length of the diagonal of a basketball court if the length is 1,128 inches and the width is 600 inches.

4. If the length of the diagonal of a high school basketball court is 97.75 feet and the length of the court is 84 feet, what is the measurement of the width?

5. If the length of the diagonal on a junior high basketball court is 85 feet and the width of the court is 42 feet, what is the measurement of the length?

Name ______________________________

QUIZ 40

Mean, Median, Mode, and Range

Find the following for the points earned by the players and team defense below:

1. Range
2. Mean
3. Median
4. Mode

Jesse Wade	$\frac{15}{48}$
Ty Johnson	$\frac{1}{8}$
Josh Maris	$\frac{3}{12}$
Ollie Mays	$\frac{1}{3}$
D. J. Tucker	$\frac{15}{48}$
Tao Faumuina	$\frac{1}{8}$
Angel Ramos	$\frac{3}{16}$
Tigers	$\frac{4}{48}$

Name ____________________

QUIZ 41

Probability

1. Last year, Tom Madsen threw 20% of his passes to the left side of the field, 40% to the right side, and 40% straight downfield. What is the probability that Madsen's first pass this year will be to his left side?

2. In how many ways can you express the outcome if the probability of an event occurring is 25%?

3. If the probability that an event will occur is .45, what is the probability that the event will not occur?

4. The letters in "monte panginny" are placed in a hat. Find the probability of the following random events:
   A. Selecting the letter *n*

   B. Selecting the letters *e, y,* or *n*

   C. Selecting any letter except *i*

In exercises 5–8, you are given $P(Q)$, the probability that a player will rush for 100 yards in a given game. Find $P(\text{Not } Q)$, the probability that event Q will not occur.

5. $P(Q) = \frac{45}{48}$ $\quad$ $P(\text{Not } Q) =$

6. $P(Q) = .435$ $\quad$ $P(\text{Not } Q) =$

7. $P(Q) = 39\%$ $\quad$ $P(\text{Not } Q) =$

8. $P(Q) = 1$ $\quad$ $P(\text{Not } Q) =$

Name ____

QUIZ 42

Circle Graphs

Based on the data below, find the measurement of the central angles in each player's portion of the circle graph.

Jesse Wade	$\frac{29}{48}$
Ty Johnson	$\frac{3}{8}$
Josh Maris	$\frac{1}{12}$
Ollie Mays	$\frac{1}{3}$
D. J. Tucker	$\frac{5}{48}$
Tao Faumuina	$\frac{1}{8}$
Angel Ramos	$\frac{1}{24}$
Tigers	$\frac{6}{48}$

Name ____

QUIZ 43

Stem-and-Leaf Plots and Histograms

The point totals (in 48ths) for a team for 16 weeks follow. Using graph paper, construct a stem-and-leaf plot and histogram based on the following data.

83	45	48	91	74	87	98	78
102	86	119	77	115	95	68	77

Name ____________________

QUIZ 44

Scatter Plots

The table below lists the total points scored (*PS*) for 10 games, along with the corresponding temperature (*T*) for each game. Using graph paper, construct a scatter plot based on the data. Does the scatter plot have a positive or negative correlation? Explain your answer.

PS	***T***
76	93
16	45
34	77
53	91
67	84
10	22
36	80
22	34
17	42
49	79

Name ______________________________

QUIZ 45

Box-and-Whisker Plots

Use graph paper to construct a box-and-whisker plot based on the following data.

Carson Clark	$\frac{35}{48}$
Ronnie Strutgart	$\frac{5}{8}$
Michael Hovay	$\frac{7}{8}$
Lars Ferguson	$\frac{2}{48}$
Joey Moore	$\frac{3}{8}$
Marcus Bleeds	$\frac{1}{6}$
Doug Savoy	$\frac{1}{4}$
Tigers	$\frac{1}{2}$

Name ______________________________

QUIZ 46

Statements Using Math Terminology

(Use with Handout 12)

Use Handout 12 to write five statements based on the data from week 4, and show the mathematical proof for each one.

1.

2.

3.

4.

5.

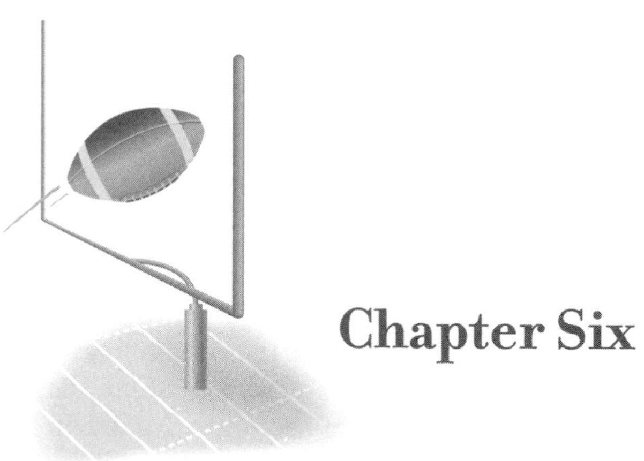

Chapter Six

Assessment

The purpose of assessment is to gather evidence of student learning. The pretest/posttest in this section can be used to accomplish that task because it represents a compilation of the concepts used on all of the practice worksheets. That said, the pretest/posttest covers a wide range of concepts, some of which may be too advanced for younger students. If that is the case, you can assign specific problems on the pretest/posttest to meet the needs of your students.

The pretest/posttest can be used as diagnostic and summative assessments. Diagnostic assessment occurs at the beginning of a unit and provides teachers with an understanding of the skills, knowledge, and learning needs students bring to the learning environment. Summative assessment occurs at the end of a period of learning and provides students with opportunities to demonstrate their achievement of the learning objectives.

Used diagnostically, giving the pretest/posttest prior to playing the Fantasy game can help you ascertain the mathematical concepts in which students need reinforcement as well as the areas in which they are strong. For example, if results from the pretest/posttest indicate that students do not yet have the skills to convert between fractions and decimals, then you probably would not use a scoring system that includes both fractions and decimals. As another example, if the pretest/posttest indicated students need more reinforcement rounding decimals, then you could integrate Practice Worksheet 7 and Quiz 7 (Rounding Decimals) into your Fantasy game.

You have the option to give the pretest/posttest at the end of the Fantasy game so you can record student achievement and growth over time as it relates to the content of the unit. Comparing the results of these two tests can yield empirical data in terms of the concepts students need to improve on and areas of strength. Data from the results given after playing the Fantasy game could also be used to modify the game in the future to better meet the needs of students.

Name ______________________________

Pretest/Posttest

Show all of your work.

1. Find the sum of the points earned by the following players:

Jesse Wade	$\frac{36}{48}$	D. J. Tucker	$\frac{2}{3}$
Ty Johnson	$\frac{5}{8}$	Tao Faumuina	$\frac{5}{16}$
Josh Maris	$\frac{21}{48}$	Angel Ramos	$\frac{1}{4}$
Ollie Mays	$\frac{1}{2}$	Tigers	$\frac{1}{16}$

2. In problem 1, what is the ratio of the points earned by Mays to the points earned by Ramos?

3. In problem 1, convert Wade's points to a decimal and round to the nearest thousandth.

4. Evaluate

$$\frac{1}{8}(T) + \frac{1}{24}(V) + \frac{1}{48}(P + R + C) - \frac{1}{12}(I) - \frac{1}{16}(F)$$

when

$T = 3$
$V = 2$
$P = 5$
$R = 8$
$C = 9$
$I = 2$
$F = 1$

Pretest/Posttest *(Cont'd.)*

5. If one factor of $\frac{24}{48}$ is $\frac{4}{6}$, what is the second factor?

6. Write the prime factorization of 270, using exponential notation.

7. Convert $\frac{66}{48}$ into a mixed number, and write it in the simplest form.

8. Which is the greater rushing average per game: 1,225 yards in 9 games or 1,556 yards in 11 games?

9. If a player accumulated $2\frac{3}{8}$ points during the first 4 weeks of the season, how many points is he projected to earn for an entire 16-game season?

Pretest/Posttest *(Cont'd.)*

10. Based on the points earned by the players in problem 1 find the following:

    Range:

    Mean:

    Median:

    Mode:

11. Fill in the missing numbers in the patterns below:

    Donte Green $\frac{1}{24}$ $\frac{3}{48}$ $\frac{1}{12}$ ______

    Donny Taylor $\frac{1}{16}$ $\frac{1}{8}$ $\frac{9}{48}$ ______

12. The price of an autographed jersey rose from \$175 to \$345. Find the percentage of price increase.

13. If a player invests 55% of his annual salary of \$6.1 million at 8.5%, how much interest will he earn after one year?

14. A player has a practice field at his house. The dimensions of the field are 100 feet by 220 feet. Find the area of the field in square inches.

15. In problem 14, what is the length of the diagonal of the field?

Pretest/Posttest *(Cont'd.)*

16. The letters in "Lupe Crepp" are placed in a hat. Find the probability of the following random events:

    A. Selecting the letter p

    B. Selecting the letters *p*, *u*, or *c*

17. Solve for the variable in the following equation.

$$\frac{1}{8}(2) + \frac{1}{48}(P + 11 + 7) - \frac{1}{12}(2) - \frac{1}{16}(1) = \frac{37}{48}$$

Chapter Seven

Answer Keys

Practice Worksheet 1

1.

Nearest $10,000	***Nearest $100,000***	***Nearest $1,000,000***
$5,010,000	$5,000,000	$5,000,000
$3,560,000	$3,600,000	$4,000,000
$3,000,000	$3,000,000	$3,000,000
$4,100,000	$4,100,000	$4,000,000

2. $4,884,650 = $4,000,000 + $800,000 + $80,000 + $4,000 + $600 + $50
   $5,009,900 = $5,000,000 + $9,000 + $900
   $3,555,555 = $3,000,000 + $500,000 + $50,000 + $5,000 + $500 + $50 + $5
   $2,999,009 = $2,000,000 + $900,000 + $90,000 + $9,000 + $9
   $4,103,737 = $4,000,000 + $100,000 + $3,000 + $700 + $30 + $7

Practice Worksheet 2

Weeks 3, 4: 35, 5; weeks 5, 6: 105, 5; weeks 7, 8: 30, 10; weeks 9, 10: 45, 9

Practice Worksheet 3

1. \$11,172,449 2. \$91,288,179 3. \$13,041,168 4. 136 5. \$37,800,000

Practice Worksheet 4

Johnson $\frac{14}{32}$ $\frac{21}{48}$ $\frac{28}{64}$ Maris $\frac{4}{6}$ $\frac{6}{9}$ $\frac{8}{12}$ Mays $\frac{2}{8}$ $\frac{3}{12}$ $\frac{4}{16}$

Tucker $\frac{6}{16}$ $\frac{9}{24}$ $\frac{12}{32}$ Faumuina $\frac{10}{48}$ $\frac{15}{72}$ $\frac{20}{96}$ Ramos $\frac{10}{12}$ $\frac{15}{18}$ $\frac{20}{24}$

Practice Worksheet 5

2. $\frac{1}{12}$ $\frac{1}{6}$ $\frac{1}{4}$ 3. $\frac{5}{16}$ $\frac{5}{8}$ $\frac{15}{16}$ 4. $\frac{20}{48}$ 5. 1.5

Practice Worksheet 6

Week One	$.625 > .479 > .25 > .146 > .125 \geq .125$
Week Two	$.313 > .271 > .229 > .146 \geq .146 > .063 > .042$
Week Three	$.292 > .229 > .208 > .188 \geq .188 > .146 > .083$
Week Four	$.292 > .271 > .104 \geq .104 > .083 > .042$
Week Five	$.\overline{3} > .271 \geq .271 > .25 \geq .25 > .021$

Practice Worksheet 7

Table 1

Johnson	*Maris*	*Mays*	*Tucker*	*Faumuina*	*Ramos*	*Tigers*
1.3	1.3	1.4	.6	.7	.8	.3
1.25	1.33	1.44	.65	.69	.77	.25
1.250	1.333	1.438	.646	.688	.771	.250

Table 2: Answers will vary.

Practice Worksheet 8

1. $1\frac{31}{48}$ 2. $\frac{19}{24}$ 3. $1\frac{1}{24}$ 4. $2\frac{5}{24}$ 5. $1\frac{3}{8}$ 6. $\frac{48}{79}$ 7. $\frac{24}{19}$ 8. $\frac{24}{25}$ 9. $\frac{24}{53}$ 10. $\frac{8}{11}$

Practice Worksheet 9

1. $\frac{29}{48}$ 2. $\frac{41}{48}$ 3. $2\frac{37}{48}$ 4. $2\frac{19}{48}$ 5. $\frac{17}{24}$

Practice Worksheet 10

1.

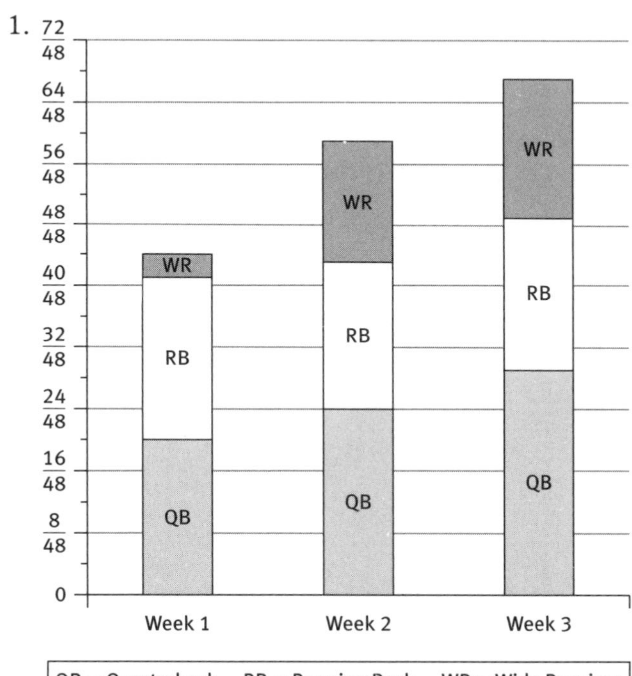

Practice Worksheet 11

1. 13 2. $\frac{7}{768}$ 3. $\frac{3}{8}$ 4. $\frac{37}{48}$ 5. 5

Practice Worksheet 12

Table 1

Wade	***Johnson***	***Maris***	***Tucker***	***Faumuina***	***Ramos***	***Tigers***
2	$1\frac{1}{2}$	$1\frac{1}{2}$	$\frac{1}{2}$	$\frac{1}{2}$	1	$\frac{1}{2}$
$1\frac{3}{4}$	$1\frac{1}{4}$	$1\frac{1}{4}$	$\frac{3}{4}$	$\frac{3}{4}$	$\frac{3}{4}$	$\frac{1}{4}$
$1\frac{7}{8}$	$1\frac{2}{8}$ or $1\frac{1}{4}$	$1\frac{3}{8}$	$\frac{5}{8}$	$\frac{6}{8}$ or $\frac{3}{4}$	$\frac{6}{8}$ or $\frac{3}{4}$	$\frac{2}{8}$ or $\frac{1}{4}$

Table 2: Answers will vary.

Practice Worksheet 13

1. 90.178 2. Day: $25,142.86; hour: $3,142.86; minute: $52.38; second: $.87
3. 23.81 hours to crawl a football field; 419.05 hours to crawl 1 mile
4. 6,510,000 ounces; 542,500 sodas 5. $143.05

Practice Worksheet 14

1. 0.2875 2. Haines, 10 mpg; Dolling, 30 mpg 3. $46,666.67 4. season ticket: $45 per ticket 5. $566,666.67

Practice Worksheet 15

1. Johnson: $1\frac{1}{4}$ 1.25 1.3 1.25 1.250 125.0% Maris: $1\frac{1}{3}$ $1.\overline{3}$ 1.3 1.33 1.333 133.3%

Mays: $1\frac{7}{16}$ 1.4375 1.4 1.44 1.438 143.8% Tucker: $\frac{31}{48}$ $.6458\overline{3}$ .6 .65 .646 64.6%

2. Answers will vary.

Practice Worksheet 16

1. 147.1% 2. 92.3% 3. 131% 4. 65.9% 5. 113.8%

Practice Worksheet 17

1. 45% 2. 12% 3. 18% 4. 66% 5. 27%

Practice Worksheet 18

1. 33% 2. 54% 3. 42% 4. $\frac{5}{12}$ 5. $\frac{5}{24}$ 6. $\frac{5}{8}$ 7. $\frac{3}{16}$

8. After year 1: 8,400 baseball fans; 16,000 football fans
After year 2: 15,540 baseball fans; 28,800 football fans
After year 3: 21,609 baseball fans; 39,040 football fans
After year 4: 26,767 baseball fans; 47,232 football fans

Practice Worksheet 19

1. 3 2. 29 3. 60 4. 1.5 5. $\frac{7}{8}$ 6. 4,588.8 7. 1,190 8. 15 in. 9. 40 ft. 10. 49.5 hours

Practice Worksheet 20

1. $\frac{1}{3}$ 2. $\frac{1}{6}$ 3. $\frac{1}{4}$ 4. $\frac{5}{8}$ 5. $\frac{13}{24}$

Practice Worksheet 21

1. 1 2. $\frac{6}{8} \times \frac{11}{6}$ 3. 5, 9 4. $\frac{8}{5}$ 5. $\frac{6}{48}$

Practice Worksheet 22

1.

Year	*Interest Earned*	*Value of Account*
1	\$369,140.63	\$6,275,390.63
2	\$392,211.91	\$6,667,602.54

2. \$12,750 \$162,750

3.

Year	*Depreciation Amount*	*Value of Car*
1	\$15,000	\$135,000
2	\$13,500	\$121,500
3	12,150	109,350

4.

Year	*Appreciation*	*Value of House*
1	\$850,000	\$9,350,000
2	\$935,000	\$10,285,000

Practice Worksheet 23

Week 1: $2 \times 3 \times 11$; week 2: prime; week 3: 2×19; week 4: 2×5^2; week 5: 2×53; week 6: $2 \times 3 \times 11$; week 7: 3×23; the five prime numbers: 2, 3, 5, 7, 11

Practice Worksheet 24

1. 6.912×10^6 2. $5.\overline{3} \times 10^3$ 3. 4.32×10^7 4. 4.32×10^9 5. $4{,}32 \times 10^3$ 6. 2.675×10^1 7. 5.0×10^{-6} 8. 7.77×10^{-4} 9. 8.77875665×10^5 10. 1.0060007×10^6 11. .09002 12. 312.5

Practice Worksheet 25

1. −32, −21, −17, −9, −3, −1, 11, 21, 44, 45, 76 2. −55, −41, −34, −33, −3, −2, 7, 12, 21, 41

3. $-5\frac{5}{16}, -3\frac{7}{8}, -2.888, -.011998, 4\frac{2}{5}, 7.004,$ 4. $.125, \frac{7}{48}, \frac{1}{6}, \frac{3}{16}, \frac{11}{48}, \frac{1}{3}$

Practice Worksheet 26

1. 370.2 2. 257 3. −208 4. 1,792 5. \$5,305,927.60 6. \$24,635,274 7. \$11,333,552

Practice Worksheet 27

1. 28 2. 18 3. 10 4. 40,320

Practice Worksheet 28

1. 3,600 inches; 9,000 centimeters 2. 375 feet 3. 53.33 yds. 4. 270,000 5. 70
6. 76 hrs.; 4,560 min.

Practice Worksheet 29

1. $\frac{23}{48}$ 2. $\frac{1}{2}$ 3. 80 4. 72

Practice Worksheet 30

1. $\frac{7}{48}C$; commutative property of addition 2. $\frac{2}{21}R$; commutative property of multiplication

3. $\left(\frac{3}{5} \cdot \frac{1}{2}\right)$; distributive property 4. $\frac{1}{4}C$; associative property of addition

5. $\frac{1}{5}P$; associative property of multiplication 6. $-\frac{9}{48}C$; inverse property of addition

7. 0; inverse property of multiplication 8. 0; identity property of addition

9. $\frac{31}{48}$; identity property of multiplication

Practice Worksheet 31

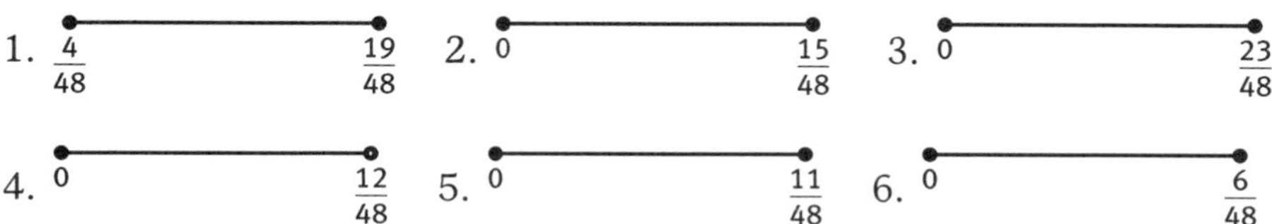

Practice Worksheet 32

1. $P = 2$ 2. $R = 3$ 3. $C = 18$ 4. $T = 2$ 5. 2 6. $\overline{3}$ 7. 1.5 8. 72 9. .5625 10. $C = 7$
11. $V = 2$ 12. $T = 3$ 13. $R = 2$ 14. $C = 7$ 15. $I = 1$ 16. $T = 3$ 17. $F = 2$ 18. $I = 1$

Practice Worksheet 33

1. $\frac{7}{48}$ 2. $\frac{19}{48}$ 3. $\frac{31}{48}$

Practice Worksheet 34

1. P = perimeter, l = length, w = width; A = area, b = base, h = height
2.

Square feet:	57,600	18,000	3.2
Square inches:	8,294,400	2,592,000	3.2
Square yards:	6,400	2,000	3.2
Square centimeters:	51,840,000	16,200,000	3.2
Square millimeters:	5,184,000,000	1,620,000,000	3.2
Square meters:	5,184	1,620	3.2

3. $2,016,000 4. $360,000
5.

	Perimeter
Professional football field	920 ft.
Soccer field	346 m.
Professional basketball court	288 ft.
High school basketball court	258 ft.

Statement 1: Answers will vary. Statement 2: Answers will vary.

Prediction		***Actual***	
Football field: prediction:	answers will vary;	actual area:	48,000 square feet
Soccer field: prediction:	answers will vary;	actual area:	7,140 square meters
Basketball court: prediction:	answers will vary;	actual area:	4,700 square feet
High school basketball court: prediction:	answers will vary;	actual area:	3,780 square feet

Practice Worksheet 35

1. Professional basketball court:	1.88	.28
Football field:	1.875	.275
College/high school basketball court:	1.68	.08
Soccer field:	1.54	.06
Junior basketball court:	1.76	.16

2. Soccer field, college/high school basketball court. 3. Answers will vary. 4. Answers will vary.

Practice Worksheet 36

1. $\frac{6}{48} \times X = Y; N = \frac{42}{48}$ 2. $\frac{1}{48} \times X = Y; N = \frac{13}{48}$ 3. $\frac{1}{16} \times X = Y; N = \frac{35}{16}$ 4. Answers will vary.

Practice Worksheet 37

1. area = 1,133.54 square feet; circumference = 119.32 ft. 2. 11.3 square feet 3. 176.625 ft. 4. diameter = 8 ft.; circumference = 25.12 ft.; area = 50.24 sq. ft. 5. radius = .796 in.; diameter = 1.59 in.; area = 1.99 sq. in.

Practice Worksheet 38

Answers will vary for all questions.

Practice Worksheet 39

1. 42.43 yds. 2. 340 ft. 3. 106.47 ft. 4. 67.82 m. 5. 71.72 yds.

Practice Worksheet 40

	Mean	*Median*	*Mode*	*Range*
1. Week 1:	.219	.135	N/A	.625
Week 2:	.151	.146	N/A	.313
Week 3:	.167	.188	N/A	.292
Week 4:	.112	.094	N/A	.292
Week 5:	.174	.25	N/A	$.\overline{3}$
Week 6:	.206	.208	N/A	.396

2. Answers will vary.

Note: N/A = not applicable.

Practice Worksheet 41

1. left 150; right 210; straight 240 2. Left $\frac{150}{600}$ or 25% 3. 9–7 4. Answers vary: $\frac{1}{4}$, .25, 5. .45

6. A. $\frac{1}{10}$ B. $\frac{3}{10}$ C. 0 D. $\frac{9}{10}$ E. $\frac{1}{100}$ F. $\frac{1}{90}$ 7. $\frac{21}{48}$ 8. .565 9. 61% 10. 0 11. 1

Practice Worksheet 42

1. Johnson: 33.5°, Maris: 108.8°, Mays: 0°, Tucker: 16.7°, Faumuina: 41.9°, Ramos: 41.9°, Tigers: 0° 2. Wade: 64.5°, Johnson: 69.9°, Maris: 64.5°, Mays: 86°, Tucker: 0°, Faumuina: 5.4°, Ramos: 69.9°, Tigers: 0° 3. Wade: 81.1°, Johnson: 54.7°, Maris: 58.3°, Mays: 62.9°, Tucker: 28.3°, Faumuina: 30.1°, Ramos: 33.7°, Tigers: 10.9° 4. 8.3% 5. 12.5% 6. 270° 7. Rounding error

Practice Worksheet 43

1.

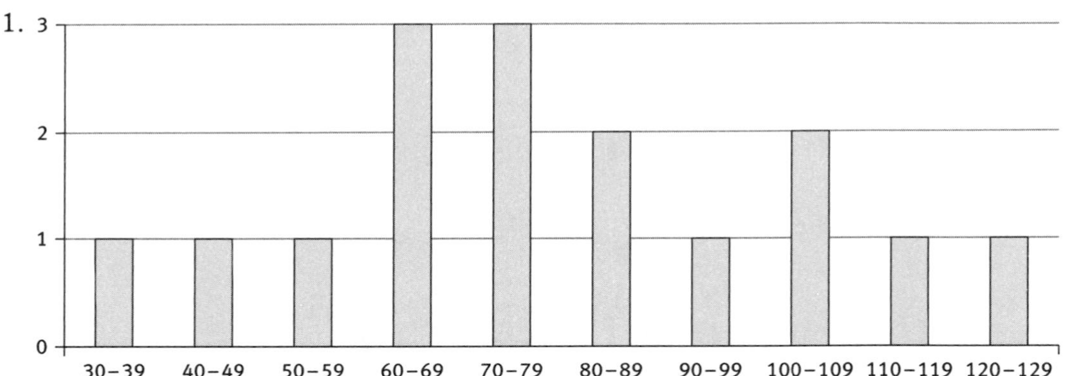

Stem	Leaf
3	8
4	9
5	0
6	6, 6, 9
7	0, 7, 9
8	5, 8
9	5
10	0, 6
11	1
12	1

2.

Stem	Leaf
0	4, 8, 9
1	0, 0, 2, 6, 7
2	1, 3, 6, 9
3	1, 4, 7
4	1

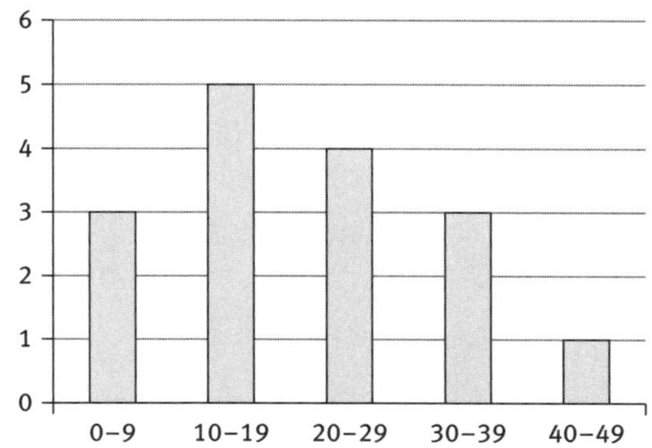

Practice Worksheet 44

1. Positive correlation

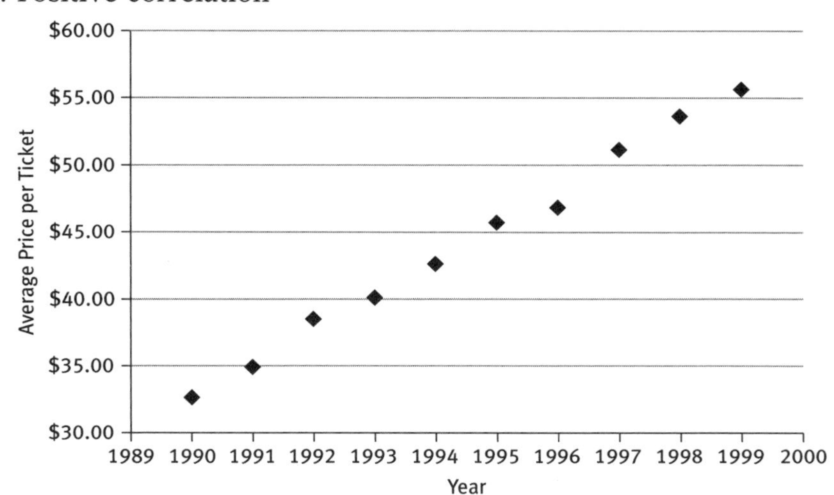

2. Positive correlation

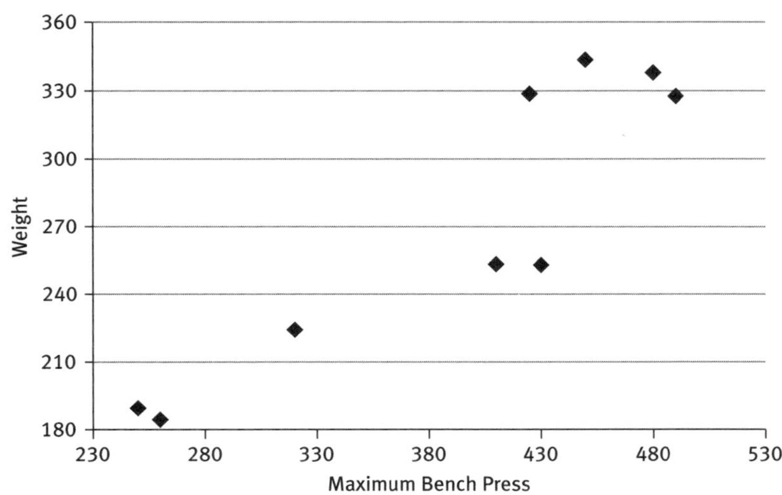

Practice Worksheet 45

1.

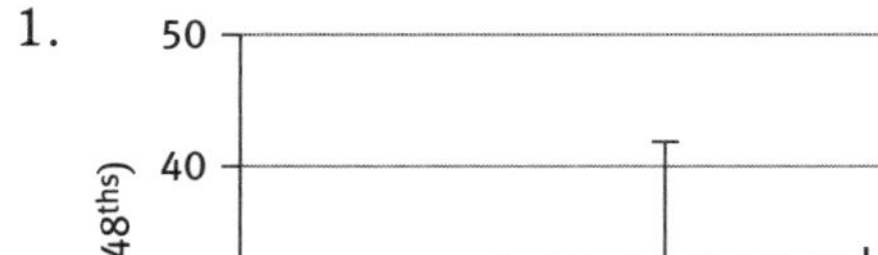

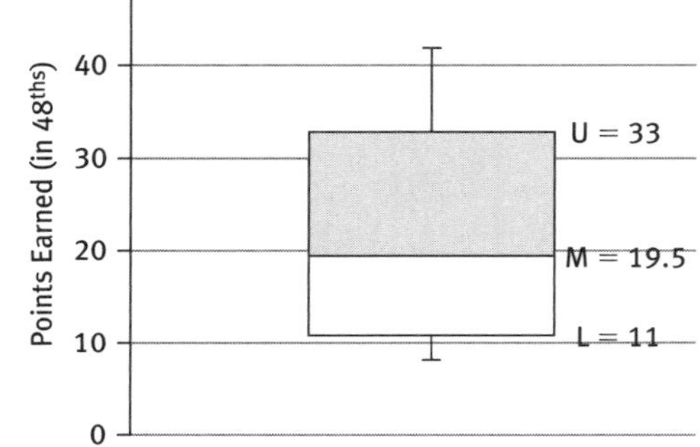

2.

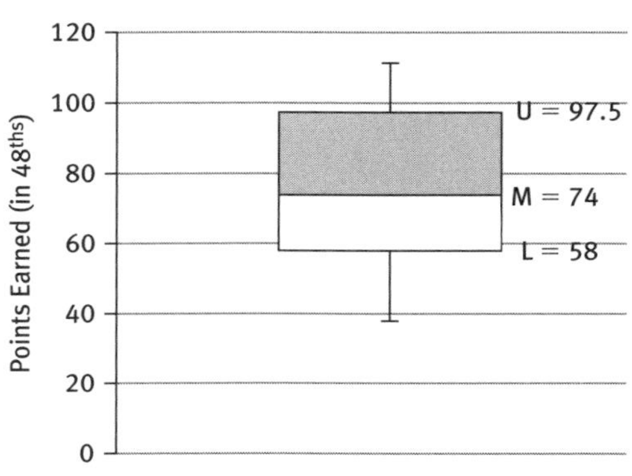

Practice Worksheet 46

1. $\frac{23}{48} + \frac{1}{4} > \frac{1}{8}$ 2. $\frac{5}{8} + \frac{23}{48}/1.75 = 63.1\%$ 3. $\frac{7}{48} \div 1.75 = 8.\overline{3}\%$ 4. $2 \times \frac{1}{8} = \frac{1}{4}$
5. $\frac{1}{2} \times \frac{1}{4} = \frac{1}{8}$ 6. $\frac{23}{48}/1.75 = 27.4\%$ 7. Answers will vary.

Extra Credit Problems

1. 18th bounce 2–5. Answers will vary.

Quiz 1

1. ***Nearest $10,000***	***Nearest $100,000***	***Nearest $1,000,000***
$4,820,000	$4,800,000	$5,000,000
$7,340,000	$7,300,000	$7,000,000
$3,340,000	$3,300,000	$3,000,000
$2,450,000	$2,400,000	$2,000,000

2. $3,556,877 = $3,000,000 + $500,000 + $50,000 + $6,000 + $800 + $70 + $7
   $6,902,889 = $6,000,000 + $900,000 + $2,000 + $800 + $80 + $9
   $9,999,009 = $9,000,000 + $900,000 + $90,000 + $9,000 + $9
   $755,555 = $700,000 + $50,000 + $5,000 + $500 + $50 + $5
3. 22,604,729; 4,930,685; 12,568,672

Quiz 2

1. 36, 12 2. 54, 9 3. 99, 3 4. 42, 21 5. 30, 3

Quiz 3

1. $113,680,331 2. $8,992,464 3. $12,831,971 4. 155.5 5. $6,006,000

Quiz 4

1. $\frac{10}{16}$ $\frac{15}{24}$ $\frac{20}{32}$ 2. $\frac{10}{32}$ $\frac{15}{48}$ $\frac{20}{64}$ 3. $\frac{24}{96}$ $\frac{36}{144}$ $\frac{48}{192}$ 4. $\frac{2}{48}$ $\frac{3}{96}$ $\frac{4}{120}$ 5. $\frac{2}{8}$ $\frac{3}{12}$ $\frac{4}{16}$

6. $\frac{26}{96}$ $\frac{39}{144}$ $\frac{52}{192}$ 7. $\frac{2}{12}$ $\frac{3}{18}$ $\frac{4}{24}$ 8. $\frac{2}{16}$ $\frac{3}{24}$ $\frac{4}{32}$

Quiz 5

1. $\frac{7}{48}$ $\frac{14}{48}$ $\frac{21}{48}$ 2. $\frac{14}{48}$ $\frac{28}{48}$ $\frac{42}{48}$ 3. $\frac{6}{48}$ $\frac{12}{48}$ $\frac{18}{48}$ 4. $\frac{10}{48}$ 5. 1.125

Quiz 6

1. $\frac{1}{8} < \frac{3}{16} < \frac{1}{4} \leq \frac{12}{48} < \frac{1}{3} \leq \frac{8}{24} < \frac{1}{2} < \frac{33}{48}$
2. $.625 > .5625 > .5 > .375 > .33 > .25 > .125 \geq .125$

Quiz 7

1. 1.1	1.3	.9	1.4	1.1	1.6	.4
1.06	1.31	.92	1.35	1.13	1.65	.38
1.063	1.313	.917	1.354	1.125	1.646	.375

2. Answers will vary.

Quiz 8

1. $1\frac{3}{4}$ 2. $\frac{7}{8}$ 3. $1\frac{5}{48}$ 4. $2\frac{15}{48}$ 5. $1\frac{7}{12}$ 6. $1\frac{7}{8}$ 7. $2\frac{1}{2}$ 8. $\frac{4}{7}$ 9. $\frac{8}{7}$ 10. $\frac{48}{53}$ 11. $\frac{16}{37}$
12. $\frac{12}{19}$ 13. $\frac{8}{15}$ 14. $\frac{2}{5}$

Quiz 9

1. $\frac{7}{12}$ 2. $1\frac{7}{48}$ 3. $\frac{11}{16}$ 4. $\frac{5}{24}$ 5. $\frac{19}{24}$

Quiz 10

1.

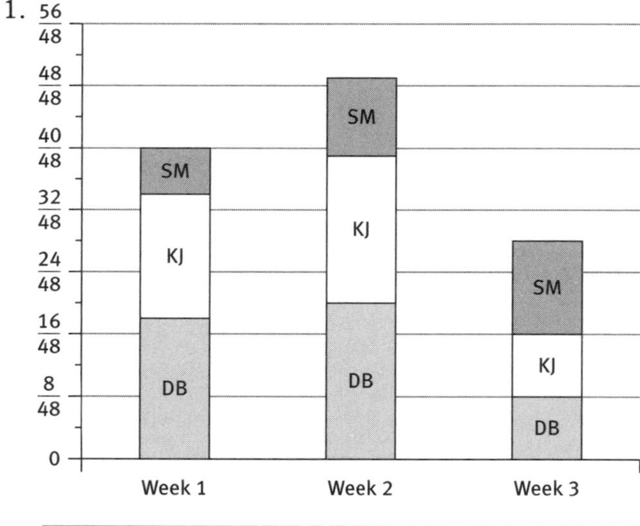

Quiz 11

1. 6 2. $\frac{11}{384}$ 3. $1\frac{1}{4}$ 4. $\frac{37}{96}$ 5. 3

Quiz 12

1.

Wade	***Mays***	***Tucker***	***Maris***	***Tigers***
1	1	$\frac{1}{2}$	1	0
1	$\frac{3}{4}$	$\frac{1}{4}$	1	$\frac{1}{4}$
1	$\frac{7}{8}$	$\frac{3}{8}$	1	$\frac{1}{8}$

2.

Wade	***Mays***	***Tucker***	***Maris***	***Tigers***
1	1	$\frac{1}{2}$	$\frac{1}{2}$	0
1	$\frac{3}{4}$	$\frac{2}{4}$ or $\frac{1}{2}$	$\frac{2}{4}$ or $\frac{1}{2}$	$\frac{1}{4}$
1	$\frac{7}{8}$	$\frac{3}{8}$	$\frac{5}{8}$	$\frac{1}{8}$

Quiz 13

1. 92.378 2. day: $30,857.14; hour: $3,857.14; minute: $64.29; second: $1.07 3. 1,111.11 minutes 4. 387,500 oz. 5. $180

Quiz 14

1. 20 ounces = .24 per ounce 2. Jolson, 15 mpg; Slammer, 30 mpg 3. 75 acres for $1.5 million = $20,000 per acre 4. $65 5. $116,666.67

Quiz 15

1.			2.		
A.	.416	.417	A.	$\frac{825}{1000}$	82.5
B.	.666	.667	B.	$\frac{5625}{10000}$	56.25
C.	.250	.250	C.	$\frac{125}{1000}$	12.5
D.	.2916	.292	D.	$\frac{5}{10}$	50
E.	.500	.500	E.	$\frac{3333}{10000}$	33.33
F.	.625	.625	F.	$\frac{375}{1000}$	37.5
G.	.250	.250	G.	$\frac{25}{100}$	25
H.	.3125	.313			

Quiz 16

1. 17 2. 9.80 3. $9\frac{9}{48}$ 4. 1 5. $\frac{5}{48}$

Quiz 17

1. 160% 2. 8.57% 3. 10% 4. 6% 5. 4.2%

Quiz 18

1. 25% 2. $\frac{50}{48}$ 3. $\frac{15}{48}$ 4. $\frac{27}{48}$ 5. $\frac{4}{48}$

Quiz 19

1. $6\frac{1}{6}$ 2. 12 3. 48 4. 2.25 5. $1\frac{5}{16}$

Quiz 20

1. $\frac{3}{16}$ 2. $1\frac{1}{2}$ 3. $1\frac{9}{16}$ 4. $\frac{6}{16} = \frac{3}{8}$ 5. $2\frac{5}{8}$

Quiz 21

1. 1 2. $\frac{1}{48}$ Josh Maris and Ty Johnson 3. $\frac{1}{12}$ 4. $\frac{3}{32}$

Quiz 22

1.

Year	*Interest Earned*	*Account Value*
1	$432.250	$6,607,250
2	$462,507.50	$7,069,757.50
3	$494,883.03	$7,564,640.53

2. $32,300, $412,000

3.

Year	*Depreciated Amount*	*Value of Car*
1	38,000	342,000
2	34,200	307,800
3	30,780	277,020

4.

Year	*Appreciation*	*Value of House*
1	850,000	9,350,000
2	935,000	10,285,000

Quiz 23

Week 1: 5×11; week 2: $2^3 \times 3^2$; week 3: 7^2; week 4: $2 \times 3 \times 5^2$; week 5: $3^2 \times 7$; week 6: 3; week 7: $2 \times 3 \times 7$; week 8: 3×17

The first five prime numbers: 2, 3, 5, 7, 11

Quiz 24

1. 5.76×10^4 2. 8.2944×10^6 3. 6.4×10^3 4. 5.184×0^7 5. 5.184×0^9 6. $5{,}184 \times 0^3$ 7. 1.11675×10^3 8. 1.1428571×10^1 9. 7.5×10^{-4} 10. 5.0025×10^2 11. .006004 12. 438,111,110,000,000

Quiz 25

1. −32, −23, −17, −11, −9, −1, 3, 21, 21, 44, 76 2. −55, −41, −21, −12, −3, 2, 7, 24, 41, 53 3. $\frac{1}{48}$ $\frac{1}{4}$ $\frac{1}{4}$ $\frac{13}{48}$ $\frac{13}{48}$ $\frac{1}{3}$ 4. $-15.004, -13\frac{1}{3}, -2.8, -1.2, .998, 7\frac{1}{6}$

5. 0 .042 .083 .104 .104 .271 .292

Quiz 26

1. 1,450 per season, 91 per game. 2. −170 3. −176 4. 896 5. \$−21,542,203

Quiz 27

1. 35 2. 45 3. 21 4. 5,040

Quiz 28

1. 1,440 in., 3,600 cm 2. 285 ft. 3. 0.57 4. 27,000 cm 5. 60 hrs. 6. 101 hrs. 6,060 min.

Quiz 29

1. $\frac{35}{48}$ 2. $\frac{11}{48}$ 3. $\frac{3}{4}$ 4. 84.71 5. 73.47

Quiz 30

Examples of properties will vary. 1. $\frac{2}{16} \times \frac{27}{48}$; distributive property 2. $\frac{9}{48}C$; commutative property of addition 3. $\frac{17}{48}R$; commutative property of multiplication 4. $-\frac{11}{17}P$; inverse property of addition 5. $\frac{2}{3}P$; associative property of multiplication

Quiz 31

1. $\frac{9}{48}$ $\frac{14}{48}$ 2. $\frac{4}{48}$ $\frac{13}{48}$ 3. $\frac{12}{48}$ $\frac{15}{48}$ 4. 0 $\frac{16}{48}$ 5. $\frac{2}{48}$ $\frac{13}{48}$

Quiz 32

1. $T = 3$ 2. $P = 15$ 3. $V = 1$ 4. $R = 10$ 5. $w = 7$ 6. $w = .236$ 7. $S = 2$ 8. $A = 720$

Quiz 33

1. $\frac{11}{48}$ 2. $\frac{2}{3}$ 3. $\frac{9}{16}$

Quiz 34

1. A. 6,400 B. 8,294,400 C. 51,840,000 2. $2,592,000

3.

L	W	P	A
		38	60
	3	30	
5	24		
	8		40
	7	29	
10			105
162.5			24,375

4. Yes: 4 × 4, 2 × 8 5. Yes: 4 × 4, 2 × 6

Quiz 35

Football field	2.26	.66
Soccer field	1.54	.06
Professional court	1.88	.28
College/high school basketball court	1.65	.05
Junior basketball court	1.79	.19

1. Soccer field, college/high school basketball court. 2–3. Answers will vary.

Quiz 36

1. $\frac{3}{48} \times X = Y,\ n = \frac{21}{48}$ 2. $\frac{15}{48} \times X = Y,\ n = \frac{195}{48}$ 3. $\frac{1}{16} \times X = Y,\ n = \frac{12}{16}$

4. Answers will vary.

Quiz 37

1. area = 1,017 sq. ft., circumference = 113 2. 5.66 ft. 3. 50.24 sq. ft. 4. diameter = 10 ft., circumference = 31.4 ft., area = 78.5 sq. ft. 5. radius = 1.5 in., diameter = 3 in., area = 7.065 sq. in.

Quiz 38

Answers will vary for all questions.

Quiz 39

1. 42.43 yds. 2. 393.95 ft. 3. 1,277.65 in. 4. 50 ft. 5. 73.9 ft.

Quiz 40

1. $\frac{12}{48}$ 2. $\frac{83}{384}$ 3. $\frac{10.5}{48}$ 4. None.

Quiz 41

1. 20%   2. .25, $\frac{1}{4}$ 3. .55   4. A. $\frac{4}{13}$ B. $\frac{6}{13}$ C. $\frac{12}{13}$ 5. $\frac{3}{48}$ 6. .565   7. 61%   8. 0

Quiz 42

Angle measurements: Wade 121°, Johnson 75°, Maris 17°, Mays 67°, Tucker 21°, Faumuina 25°, Ramos 8°, Tigers 25°

Quiz 43

Stem	Leaf
4	5, 8
5	
6	8
7	4, 7, 7, 8
8	3, 6, 7
9	1, 5, 8
10	2
11	5, 9

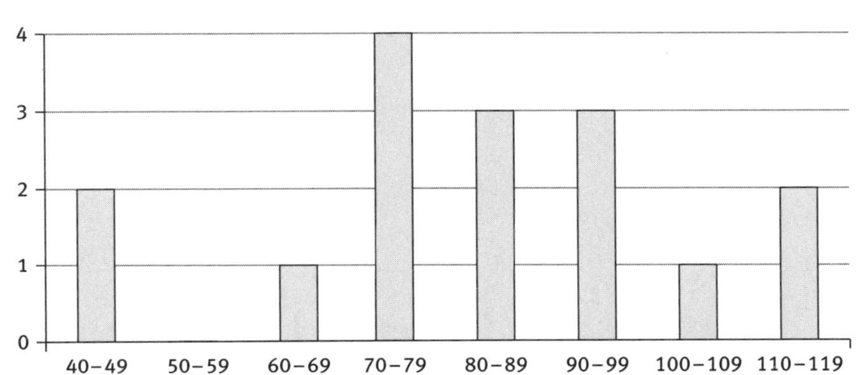

Quiz 44

Positive correlation

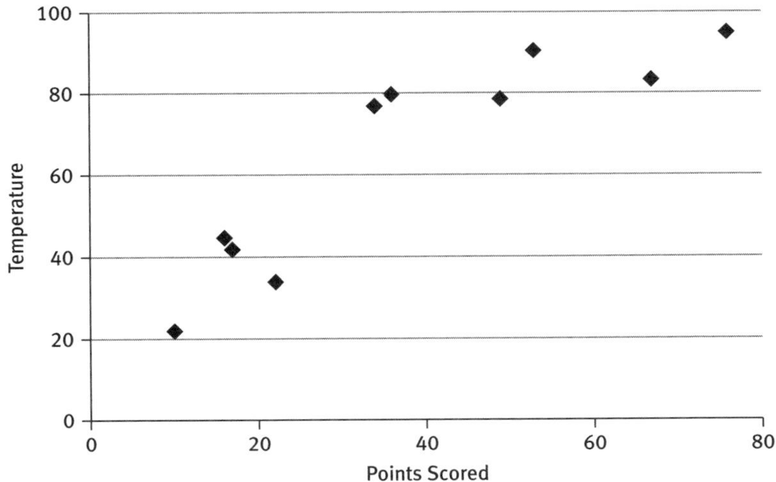

Quiz 45

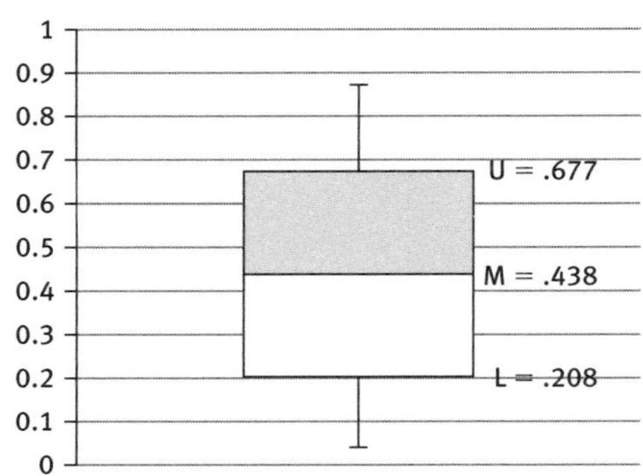

Quiz 46

Answers will vary.

Pretest/Posttest

1. $3\frac{29}{48}$ 2. 2 : 1 3. .750 4. $\frac{11}{16}$ 5. $\frac{6}{8}$ 6. $2 \times 3 \times 3 \times 3 \times 5$ 7. $1\frac{3}{8}$ 8. 1,556 in 11 games

9. $9\frac{1}{2}$ 10. range: $\frac{33}{48}$; mean: $\frac{173}{384}$; median: $\frac{22.5}{48}$; mode: None 11. $\frac{5}{48}$, $\frac{12}{48}$ 12. 97%

13. $285,175 14. 3,168,000 15. 241.66 ft. 16. A. $\frac{3}{9}$ B. $\frac{5}{9}$ 17. $P = 2$

Appendix: Lesson Plans

How to Begin the Game

You may wish to administer the Pretest (see Chapter Six) before the game begins.

The handouts in this text and in the accompanying student workbooks are the same.

Please do not despair if Lesson 2 or 3 does not go as smoothly as planned. When I first introduced the game to students, it wasn't until the third week that students began to master the computational process for their teams. If you can hang in there, your students will be rewarded with a rich learning experience full of excitement.

Lesson 1

Distribute Handouts 1 and 2, and review them with students. (If students do not have student workbooks, I recommend they keep all their Fantasy Football and Math materials together in a folder.) Have students select their players.

Homework: Students complete their team roster, staying under the salary cap, and complete Handout 2.

Lesson 2

Distribute Handouts 3, 5, and 6 (you may also want to hand out the partial box score for the Panthers at Tigers). Teach students how to read box scores and how to compute points. Then have students practice computing points for players on the Wildcats using Handout 3.

Homework: Students complete Handout 6.

Lesson 3

Distribute Handouts 4, 9, and 11. In addition, hand out box scores from the previous week's games, or let students access data online. Have students compute the points their players earned the first week on Handout 9. If time permits when they have finished, they trade papers with a classmate, and each verifies the other's computations. If the computations are correct, have students sign their name at the top of their classmate's worksheet. Students can then post their confirmed scores on the Fantasy Football bulletin board, using Handout 11.

Lesson 4

Show students how to construct multiple-line, stacked-bar, and circle graphs. (Note that circle graphs may be too advanced for younger students.) For the stacked-bar and multiple-line graphs, particular attention needs to be given to the intervals on the *y*-axis (see the last paragraph in Chapter Three).

Continuing the Game: How to Integrate Worksheets

Each week students compute points, update graphs, and complete worksheets that dovetail with concepts they are studying in their textbook. As soon as students are comfortable with computing points (usually after a few weeks, depending on grade level), you can introduce the total points equations (Handouts 7, 8, and 10).

By integrating practice worksheets into your existing curriculum, you will maximize the thematic approach to mathematics that the game provides. For example, if your students are learning how to round decimals, you can use Worksheet 7, in which students round decimals. In this way, students are presented with opportunities to reinforce math concepts that tie in with the game. This approach helps them make connections between math in school and math in the real world.

Each week one or more worksheets can be integrated into your math lessons. Some worksheets (for example, Practice Worksheet 40: Mean, Median, Mode, and Range) can be used for several weeks because students perform operations based on the points earned by their players for a given week. Other worksheets are used to compute cumulative points earned for the first few weeks of the season. These worksheets serve a cumulative effect because students receive multiple exposures to the same material on a weekly basis. As the season progresses, students may in fact be working on several worksheets each week. This process provides students with multiple exposures to content, thereby facilitating mastery. For these reasons, it is highly recommended that students also do the graphing activities, for weekly exposures to circle, stacked-bar, and multiple-line graphs will help them comprehend the material.

Students can also create their own worksheets based on their team's performance. For instance, if students are learning how to add and subtract fractions, they can write problems based on the points their players earn—for example, "If player A earned three-eighths and player B earned four-fifths, how many total points did they earn?"

Tips and Suggestions

• There are several ways to verify the accuracy of students' work. As previously stated, students can sign their name at the top of a peer's worksheet to verify their work. Second, when students compute points, they can write the points earned for their players on the board. When several students post the same points earned for a player, they are probably on the right track. Students can use this information as a guide to check their work. However, they cannot simply copy the points from the board because they still have to show their work on their worksheets. In addition, advanced students can compute points using both positive and negative versions of the same equation, since both answers will result in the same absolute value.

• You can assess students using the pretest/posttest, 46 quizzes in this text, or have students compute points for your team using a scoring system you choose. Because you have a fantasy team of your own, you've already computed your points and have the answers. Students can also construct one or more of the three types of graphs based on your team for a given week.

• Students can create their own scoring systems and use them to compute points. To do this, they will need to evaluate scoring systems that they have already used, which gives them opportunities to use evaluation, the highest-level thinking skill according to Bloom's Taxonomy.

• You can also play Fantasy Football and Mathematics in groups. Place students in triads to compute aggregate points. Then the different groups compete against each other. Thus, two games can run concurrently: one game for individuals and another game for groups.

• Another alternative is that students can have more than one team. They can also play two sports at once. For instance, the schedule for professional football and basketball seasons overlaps in November and December, so students could play both fantasy sports concurrently.

• You can also play two games of Fantasy Football and Mathematics. Halfway through the season, students can draft new teams. This gives hope to students whose teams do not perform well during the first game. Students will be excited and highly motivated to draft new teams.

• Dedicating a bulletin board to the game is a must. Students can post their teams, graphs, statistics, trades, and team rankings. You can include a "Wall of Fame," in which students post the most valuable players or the best bargains according to the salary cap. Conversely, you can also include a "Wall of Shame" in which students post the least productive players according to the salary cap.

• You can also construct a large bulletin board in the shape of a football field. Each student is represented on the bulletin board by a football that gradually progresses down the field from week to week as the season unfolds. This is an effective way to visualize the rankings of the students' teams.

• You can link Fantasy Football and Mathematics to other disciplines. For example, you can post a map of the United States in which students can mark the cities that host professional football teams. You can give students blank maps in which they name the cities and states in which the football teams are located.

• Students can make their own spreadsheets to list their teams, weekly scores, and cumulative scores. They can also use computer programs to construct a variety of graphs.

• Each week students can be given an expository writing assignment in which they write about the math concepts they used and explain what they learned. A similar assignment can also be given at the end of the game.

• Students can also conduct research. For example, they can write a report on their favorite player that includes the community service the player has been involved in, a history of the area where the player was born, or the college the player attended. Researching colleges that players attended can be the first exposure students get to higher education; perhaps this exposure can help students to set goals toward attending college themselves.

• Prizes? You can take the top three and bottom three team owners to lunch, throw Fantasy Football pizza or ice cream parties, or inscribe the winner's name on an inexpensive trophy each year, which would then stay at the school in perpetuity.

• Finally, you can make the transition into Fantasy Basketball and Mathematics at the end of the football season!